Mahekpreet Kaur #14
W9-CAW-853
level
C
Rehearsing
for the Common
Core Standards
Reading
RALLY!
EDUCATION
We're all about student success!

ISBN 978-1-4204-7892-1
R 7892-1

Photo/Illustration credits: p. 8 Elizabeth Graham; p. 9 & 10 Kristina J. Nelson; p. 20 Barbara Kiwak; p. 30-32 Marty Crump, Ph.D.; p. 41 & 42 Valerie Sokolova; p. 52 & 53 Dinodia Photo Library Pvt Ltd; p. 54 Jeff Rose Photography; p. 62, 63, & 65 Gary Undercuffler; p. 75 & 76 Apryl Stott; p. 85-87 Tony Helies; p. 96 Debbie Palen; p. 105-106 Old Dartmouth Historical Society, New Bedford Whaling Museum, New Bedford, MA; p. 107 Mark Corcoran; p. 117 & 118 Jeff Crosby; p. 127 ©Reydesign/Dreamstime.com; p. 138-139 Alan Stonebraker; p. 148 (top right) Sarah Owens; p. 148 (bottom) David Liebman; p. 149 Wolfgang Kaehler; p. 150 Getty Images; p. 159 John C.H. Grabill Collection, Library of Congress, LC-DIG-ppmsc-02634; p. 160 Library of Congress, Prints & Photographs Division, Detroit Publishing Company Collection, LC-D4-13756; p. 162 PhotoDisc, Inc.; p. 172 & 173 Allan Eitzen; p. 183 & 184 Sherry Shahan; p. 185 (top left) Rocky Fuller; p. 185 (bottom right) & 186 Nationwide Children's Hospital; p. 194-196 Bob McMahon; p. 206-207 Vesterheim Norwegian-American Museum; p. 217 & 220 Phyllis Harris; p. 229 & 232 Dani Sneed; p. 241 & 242 Matt Smith; p. 251 Warren Heise; p. 252 Chris Dietel; p. 253-254 Scott Linstead; p. 263 Chris Sippel; p. 265 Barbara Knutson.

0813.MAQ

RALLY! EDUCATION • 22 Railroad Avenue, Glen Head, NY 11545 • (888) 99-RALLY

Contents

Literary (L), Informational (I), and Paired Passages with Multiple Choice, Short Response, Extended Response, and Essay Questions

Introduction

Rehearsing for the Common Core Standards

Rehearsing for the Common Core Standards: Reading prepares students for the types of tasks, assessments, and tests they may be asked to complete to demonstrate they have the skills listed in the Common Core Reading Standards.

This book includes features expected of Common Core material, including using authentic and complex passages, focusing on close reading and using text-based evidence, and asking complex questions that require students to analyze, critique, and make connections.

Common Core Reading Standards

The Common Core Reading Standards are divided into two parts: Reading Standards for Literature and Reading Standards for Informational Text. These two parts are each divided into three main subtopics, with specific skills listed in each subtopic.

In this book, each subtopic is covered in turn in the first three sections. The final section combines all the subtopics to provide complete coverage of all the skills.

Section	Subtopic	Informational Text Standards Addressed	Literature Standards Addressed
Part A	Key Ideas and Details	Standards 1, 2, and 3	Standards 1, 2, and 3
Part B	Craft and Structure	Standards 4, 5, and 6	Standards 4, 5, and 6
Part C	Integration of Knowledge and Ideas	Standards 7, 8, and 9	Standards 7 and 9
Part D	All Together	All Standards	All Standards

Passage and Question Formats

Each section of the book contains both literary and informational passages, and several sets of paired passages are also included throughout the book. Each passage or set of passages is followed by a set of ten questions. The ten questions cover all the standards of the subtopic, and many questions cover more than one standard.

Rehearsing for the Common Core Standards: Reading includes a range of question types. Each section of the book contains multiple choice, graphic organizer, short response, extended response, and essay questions.

Part A:

Key Ideas and Details

Literary and Informational Passages with Multiple Choice, Short Response, Extended Response, and Essay Questions

Common Core State Standards for Informational Text (Grade 3)

RI.3.1 Ask and answer questions to demonstrate understanding of a text, referring explicitly to the text as the basis for the answers.

RI.3.2 Determine the main idea of a text; recount the key details and explain how they support the main idea.

RI.3.3 Describe the relationship between a series of historical events, scientific ideas or concepts, or steps in technical procedures in a text, using language that pertains to time, sequence, and cause/effect.

Common Core State Standards for Literary Text (Grade 3)

RL.3.1 Ask and answer questions to demonstrate understanding of a text, referring explicitly to the text as the basis for the answers.

RL.3.2 Recount stories, including fables, folktales, and myths from diverse cultures; determine the central message, lesson, or moral and explain how it is conveyed through key details in the text.

RL.3.3 Describe characters in a story (e.g., their traits, motivations, or feelings) and explain how their actions contribute to the sequence of events.

Directions: Read the passage. Then answer the questions that follow it.

Crayon Artist

By Sara Matson

Kristina Nelson has crafted a career with a box of crayons.

1 Kristina Nelson remembers being a third-grader. The girl who sat next to her had a big box of crayons, and Kristina had only a small box. Kristina wanted a big box. She loved to draw. She had no idea then that she would grow up to use crayons to create colorful drawings of animals, people, pancakes, pears, and even toilet paper.

2 After she finished college, Kristina traveled to Mexico to teach art at an elementary school. She wasn't sure if her students would have art supplies, so she took an entire suitcase of crayons with her. "In fact," Kristina says, "I didn't bring that many clothes. I was borrowing other teachers' clothes."

3 It turned out that Kristina's students didn't need all the crayons, so one day, she says, "I decided to use them. I found a little store that sold paper near my house, and started to create crayon drawings."

4 When Kristina returned home to the United States, her mom saw her artwork. "You should make more crayon drawings!" her mom said.

Practice, Practice, Practice

5 Kristina's mom introduced her to a professional crayon artist named Don Marco. He had been working with crayons for more than 25 years. He offered to give Kristina lessons.

6 Kristina accepted Don Marco's offer. "Sometimes I worked with him six days a week!" she says. "I practiced and practiced and practiced what he taught me." After a year and a half, Kristina sold her first crayon drawing. Now she has a studio where she draws, displays, and sells her crayon art.

7 Kristina believes in practice, and she believes in education. The road to becoming a better artist is to "read many books on art," she says. "Educate yourself. Take art classes and visit museums. Other artists and their art will teach you to make your artwork better." But, she adds, "Even if your artwork is never sold, that is just fine. Just the joy of making artwork is what counts."

Drawing a Pear Kristina's Way

You will need

a pear
a pencil
a box of crayons
tan or beige construction paper

1 In pencil, sketch the shape of a pear on tan or beige construction paper.

2 Now take a good look at the colors on your pear. Color in the yellow parts.

3 Do you see green on your pear? Add shades of green to your drawing.

4 Add shadows to the pear. Is there orange, brown, or white on your pear? Add those colors.

Now that's a nice-looking pear!

Tip

Sharpen your crayon with a crayon sharpener. As you twist the crayon, tilt it upward to get a rounded, slightly pointed tip. Too sharp a tip will break easily.

Directions: Answer the following questions. If you need more space to write an answer, write your answer on your own paper.

1 Which sentence best supports the idea that Kristina is a successful crayon artist?

A "She had no idea then that she would grow up to use crayons to create colorful drawings of animals, people, pancakes, pears, and even toilet paper."

B "When Kristina returned home to the United States, her mom saw her artwork."

C "Kristina's mom introduced her to a professional crayon artist named Don Marco."

D "Now she has a studio where she draws, displays, and sells her crayon art."

2 According to the activity, the tip of a crayon should not be too sharp because

A it might break

B it might tear the paper

C it needs to color in areas easily

D it needs to outline the item well

3 Paragraphs 2 and 3 describe Kristina's trip to Mexico. Why are these details important in the article? What do they show about Kristina's career? Use details from the article to support your answer.

These details are important because Paragraphs 2 & 3 describe Kristina's Trip to Mexico & tell about her career & as she turned a hobbie into a career.

4 How does the author emphasize how many crayons Kristina took to Mexico? What does this detail suggest about how many crayon drawings she created? Use details from the article to support your answer.

The author emphasizes how Many crayons Kristina brought by Saying she brought a suitcase full of crayons. This means she Made lots of drawings,

5 The first sentence of the article states that Kristina "crafted a career with a box of crayons." Why do you think the author chose the word *crafted*? Use details from the article to support your answer.

The author used crafted because He wanted the reader to think that kristina "Made a career" so Made is crafted. Crafting Means Making by hand.

6 How did Kristina's mother encourage her? Give **two** specific examples in your answer. Use details from the article to support your answer.

give support

restate

Kristina's mother encouraged her by interducing her to a proffectional crayon artist.

detail #1

Her Mom was surprised with her art. &

detail #2

Her mom saw her work She told her she should make more.

7 How does Kristina feel about her career? Do you feel she enjoys her career? Use at least **two** specific details from the article to support your answer.

I belive Kristina feels proud Of What She does & that I think that She does enjoy her career.

8 The activity in the article describes how to draw a pear. How can you tell that the pear should look real? How would having many different crayons help you achieve this? Use details from the activity to support your answer.

I can tell that the pear Should look real because then it would look like a photograph. having different crayons can help you achieve this because you need color to brighten anything.

9 Read this sentence from the article.

"Kristina believes in practice, and she believes in education."

How do Kristina's actions show that she followed this advice? Explain how she used both practice and education to become good at what she does. Use details from the article to support your answer.

Planning Space

You can complete the graphic organizer below to help plan your answer.

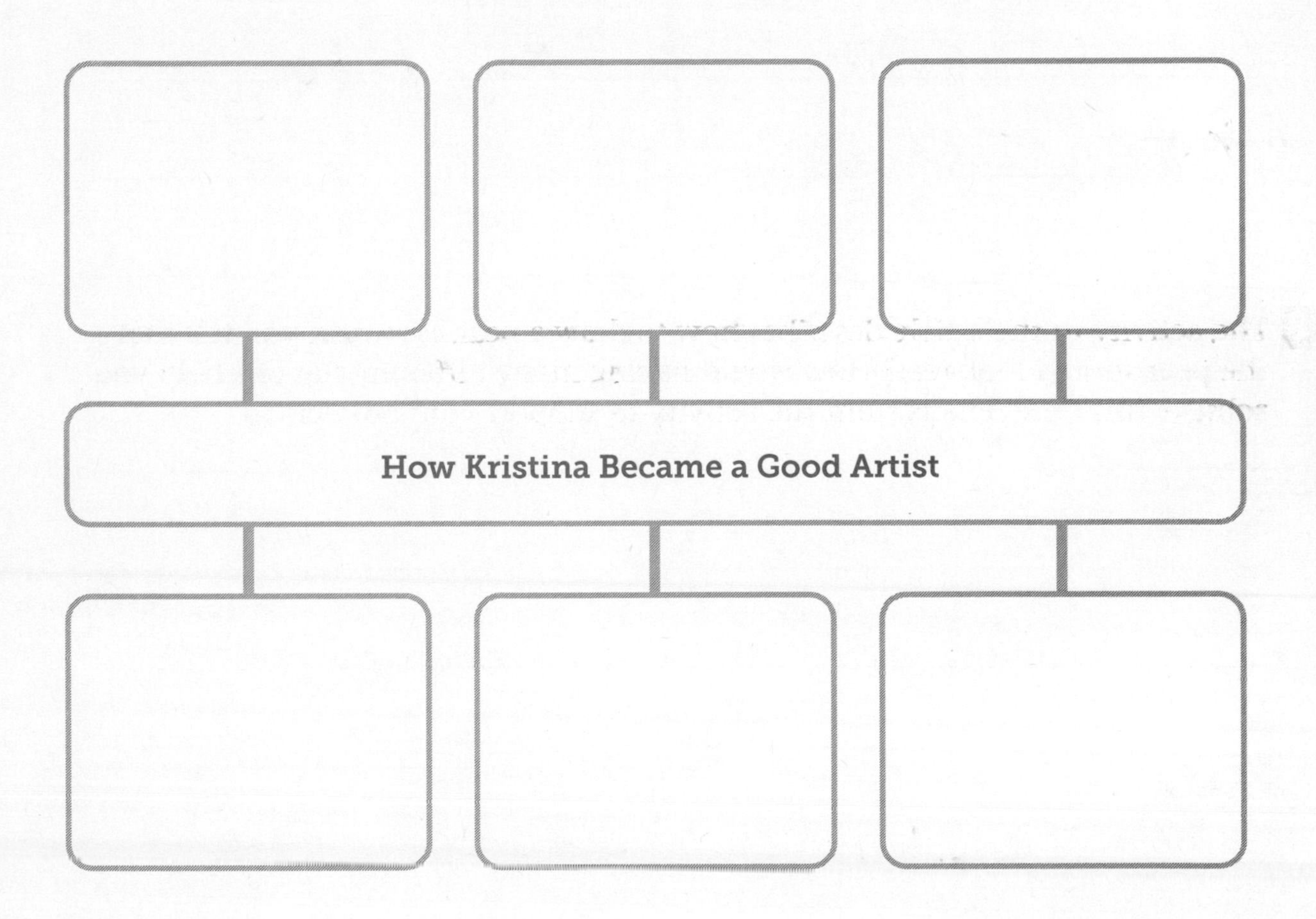

10 The article describes Kristina's career, but also includes an activity. Why do you think the author included the activity? How does it help readers understand what Kristina does? Use details from the article to support your answer.

Planning Space

You can write notes, make a list, or draw a chart to help plan your answer.

Directions: Read the passage. Then answer the questions that follow it.

Through the Ice

By Ann Devendorf

1 About a half-mile behind the big red barn on our Minnesota farm lay a pond. In summer, my brother Harry and I would run through a stand of oak trees to skip stones there. The pond wore a collar of black mud. It was not a place for swimming.

2 In late summer, the pond would be covered by a green and bubbly scum. Sometimes a stench rose from it. We stayed away.

3 When winter came, the pond was once again an inviting place. One day when ice covered it, Harry said to me, "Try walking across."

4 The ice looked solid. No water showed through it, but I hesitated.

5 "Go ahead, Sis," Harry urged. "Try it. You're lighter than I am. If the ice holds, we can run and slide on it. It'll be fun."

6 I wanted to please Harry, and I thought about the fun of a long slide on the ice. I began to take gliding steps across the pond.

7 In the middle of the pond, the ice gave way with a sudden *crack!* I flung out my arms. The next thing I knew I was hanging on to the edge of a hole in the ice by arms outstretched on the ice. From my shoulders down I hung in icy water. I thought of the bottom of the pond. I knew it would be black and awful down there, full of silt and rotting vegetation and maybe slimy creatures.

8 I tried to climb out of the hole, but when I got a knee on the ice, it broke like window glass.

9 Again and again I tried to get out. Again and again the ice shattered. The hole widened. I was wearing a coat of heavy material called plush. As it became soaked, it dragged me down. I tired of the struggle and rested with my arms stretched out on the ice.

10 I looked at Harry on shore. He seemed rooted to the spot. "I can't get out!" I screamed when I caught some breath.

11 He turned and ran from the pond. As I looked at his back, I wondered: Is he running for help, or is he running away and leaving me to slip to the bottom?

12 I was surprised to see him bend and pick up a large, fallen oak limb. It was black and V-shaped. He ran with it toward the pond. At the edge, he flopped to his stomach, pushed the limb before him, and wriggled toward me. When a slender top branch was within reach, I grabbed for it. It did not break.

13 Hand over hand, I pulled myself from the hole. I began to stand. I wanted to run from the pond as fast as I could run. Harry yelled, "Get down! Stay flat on the ice or it'll break again." I obeyed. Harry wriggled backward toward shore, towing the limb. I hung on to a branch and wriggled toward shore on my stomach.

14 Off the pond, we ran toward the house. My overshoes squished and squirted water. My clothes dripped. Near the house Harry said, "I'm making myself scarce."

invisable

15 I crashed through the kitchen door, sobbing, "I fell through the ice." Mother rushed over, unbuttoned my coat, and stripped my clothes from me. She filled a tub with hot water. The bath stopped my teeth-chattering chill, and I was able to tell her all that had happened.

16 After the bath, I was given a cup of hot milk to drink and was sent to bed. "I don't want you to get pneumonia," said Mother.

17 I heard Mother call Harry. I heard him come into the kitchen. I heard loud voices. He was being lectured about getting a younger sibling into trouble. He was sent to bed as punishment.

18 I do not think it changed him, because when summer came he wanted me to parachute from the loft of the big red barn to a small scattering of hay on the ground. He handed me a gunnysack to use as a parachute.

19 "You go first," he said. "Try it, Sis. It'll be fun."

20 But *I* had changed. I said no, and so got through the rest of my childhood safe of life and limb.

Directions: Answer the following questions. If you need more space to write an answer, write your answer on your own paper.

11 Read this sentence from paragraph 10.

"He seemed rooted to the spot."

What does this sentence suggest about Harry?

A He finds the events funny.

B He thinks his sister is playing.

C He feels too tired to help.

D He is unsure what to do.

12 In paragraph 13, why does Harry tell his sister to get down?

A He is trying to stop his sister from falling through again.

B He does not want their mother to see them.

C He finds it funny that his sister has to crawl along the ice.

D He wants to make a game of pulling her along.

13 The narrator is unsure about going on the ice, but does anyway. Give **two** reasons the narrator goes on the ice. Use details from the story to support your answer.

One reason the narrator goes on the ice because she wants to impress her brother and because She wanted to slide on the ice.

14 After falling through the ice, the narrator is unable to get out of the hole. Explain why it is difficult to get out of the hole. Include at least **two** reasons in your answer.

The narrator can't get out because the ice kept breaking and her jacket was to heavy.

Made From Plush

15 In paragraph 11, the narrator tells what she was thinking. What do these thoughts show about her relationship with her brother? Use details from the story to support your answer.

These thoughts show that she doesn't trust her brother because she thought he was running away.

16 Harry's rescue of his sister shows that he is calm under pressure. Give **two** examples of good decisions he makes that show his quick thinking. Explain why each decision is a good one.

One example is the way he saves his sister because he did not scream or go get help. Second example is when Harry gets screamed at because he does not get upset and start crying.

not

17 Is it surprising that Harry helps his sister get out of the hole in the ice? Use details from the story to support your conclusion.

Yes, because he turned around and started running away but then saves his sister.

18 Harry is older than the narrator of the story. Explain how the age difference affects the events in the story. Give at least **two** specific examples in your answer.

The age difference affects the story because if the narrator was older Harry would have been stuck in the ice and not the narrator.

19 In the last paragraphs, the narrator describes being asked to parachute off the barn. How is this event similar to being asked to walk on the ice? How is the narrator's response different? Use details from the story to support your answer.

Planning Space

You can write notes, make a list, or draw a chart to help plan your answer.

20 The story is mainly about an event where the narrator fell through the ice. How does the experience change the narrator? How does it affect her relationship with her brother? Use details from the story to support your answer.

Planning Space

You can write notes, make a list, or draw a chart to help plan your answer.

Directions: Read the passage. Then answer the questions that follow it.

Don't Dry Up, Frogs!

Story and Photos by Marty Crump, Ph.D.

1 Dry season in northern Argentina is hot. I often wore shorts and T-shirts there during my search for frogs.

2 I spent a lot of time with my Argentine friends Felix and Gaby. Like me, they are scientists. One June day, they took me on an expedition to find the perfect frog pond. We drove 50 miles along a dusty dirt road. Suddenly Felix announced, *"!Ya estamos!"* (We're here!)

3 "Are you sure?" I asked. The barren landscape reminded me of a desert back home in Arizona. It certainly didn't seem like a very froggy place to me. I saw no water ... just dust.

4 We parked the car and walked past cacti and other thorn-covered plants. When we reached an open area of dry, cracked ground, Gaby smiled and said, *"!Aqui esta el charco!"* (Here's the pond!)

5 Again, I asked if they were sure. Felix and Gaby insisted that if I returned during rainy season, I would find hundreds of frogs.

Cow Pies and Cocoons

6 Where were the frogs hiding? I did a little detective work. Near the edge of the dry pond, I turned over a log and found a warty, brown rococo toad. (Toads are a type of frog.) The dirt beneath the log was damp. That toad had found itself a good spot. I carefully replaced the log.

7 I spied a five-inch-wide burrow nearby. I peered inside but could see nothing but darkness. Frogs may have been hiding inside ... unless it was a snake's home!

8 Three tree frogs huddled together under a cow pie. This dropping was dry on the outside but moist underneath. Fortunately for them, frogs don't have much of a sense of smell.

9 Felix and Gaby assured me there were llanos frogs beneath the dry pond. These frogs burrow four to five inches into the mud. They shed up to 40 layers of skin, forming cocoons around themselves. These cocoons help to keep them from losing water. The frogs sleep underground for several months, unaware of everything above them, such as biologists searching for the perfect frog pond. When the rains start up again, water soaks into the cocoons. The frogs break out and wriggle to the surface. They're hungry and ready to eat anything smaller than they are, even other frogs.

Inside-Out Raincoat

10 We saw only one frog that day that was not hiding. It was a painted-belly monkey frog. This green frog with a brown-and-white belly clung to the tip of a thorny branch. As I touched the branch, the frog opened its eyes and stared at me. It looked perfectly comfortable out in the dry air and wind.

11 Painted-belly monkey frogs have special glands all over their skin. These glands ooze a waxy goop. In slow motion, the frog reaches

up and over its body with a leg to spread the slippery stuff. It uses all four legs, one at a time, to coat every nook and cranny of its body. When the goop dries, the frog wears a waterproof raincoat. But this raincoat works in the opposite way our raincoats work. Ours keep water out. A painted-belly monkey frog's raincoat keeps water in. And that's why these frogs don't hunker down beneath logs or burrow underground.

12 Felix and Gaby were right. Four months later, the pond overflowed with water. Eleven different kinds of frogs croaked, peeped, trilled, and chirped in their new home. My friends had shown me the perfect frog pond after all. During the rainy season, 11 different kinds of tadpoles swam about, eventually sprouted legs, lost their tails, and transformed into frogs.

Do Your Own Detective Work

13 By doing your own detective work, you can discover where your neighborhood frogs hide while waiting for rain. Use a long-handled rake to roll over logs and rocks. Always roll the log or rock toward you, just in case a scorpion or snake has made that place its home. Avoid reaching into any holes. Always return logs and rocks to their original positions. Remember, animals live under those objects. If you pick up a frog, handle it gently and return it to the same spot. It chose that spot for a reason.

14 You'll probably find some surprises, but don't count on finding any frogs that wear raincoats. Painted-belly monkey frogs live only in South America.

Directions: Answer the following questions. If you need more space to write an answer, write your answer on your own paper.

21 Why are the details in the first paragraph important to the main idea?

- **A** They help show how dry it was.
- **B** They tell what country the author is in.
- **C** They show what to wear when looking for frogs.
- **D** They suggest that looking for frogs is hard work.

22 What are the photographs on page 30 mainly included to help readers understand?

- **A** where to start searching for frogs
- **B** what frogs need to survive
- **C** how the pond changed over time
- **D** why frogs are found living near ponds

23 In the third paragraph, the author describes the "barren landscape." Explain what this means. How does this show why it does not look like a "froggy place"? Use details from the article to support your answer.

This might mean a desert of a dry landscape. Because the author says it's like the one in Afrazenea.

24 In paragraph 2, the author includes what Felix says. Why does the author give what he says in Spanish? How does this help make readers feel like they are there? Use details from the article to support your answer.

Felix says it in spanish because Aregentina's offial langlige is spanish. Because he yells in exitment.

25 In paragraphs 2 through 5, the author describes a trip to the pond to find frogs. How does the author feel about their chances of finding frogs? Explain how you can tell. Use at least **two** details from the paragraphs to support your answer.

The author would feel exited I can tell because the tittle is "Don't Dry Up frogs". & some might have dryed up already. The author asks Felix & Gabby "Are you sure"

26 In the section "Cow Pies and Cocoons," the author states that she did detective work. Complete the chart below by listing the **three** places she looked and what she found there.

Where She Looked	What She Found
1) ~~edge of dry~~ Under log ~~Pond~~,	Warty brown rococo toad.
2) Five inch wide burrow,	~~Darkness~~ nothing
3) Under a Cow pie.	three tree frogs huddled together.

27 Paragraphs 6 and 8 describe two places the author found frogs. What is similar about the two places? How does this explain why they were good spots for the frogs? Use details from the article to support your answer.

There was dryness on the places the frogs were hidding. So they wouldn't get all dryed up.

28 The section titled "Inside-Out Raincoat" describes the painted-belly monkey frog. Explain how the frog makes the raincoat and how it keeps the frog from drying out. Use details from the section to support your answer.

The frog makes the raincoat by putting on sticky stuff and it stays on.

29 The section "Do Your Own Detective Work" describes how readers can search for frogs. What warnings are given to readers in the section? How would they protect the reader and the frogs? Give at least **three** examples of warnings from the section to support your answer.

Planning Space

You can complete the chart below to help plan your answer.

Warning	Purpose of the Warning
Always roll the log or rock toward you.	To make sure no snakes & scorpins get in.
Put objects in there original postions.	animals will lose homes.
Put frog handle back.	chose a good spot.

Warnings are given
because if you want to
catch a frog it's fine
but if you want remember
to put all your items back
to were you found the am
or you might distory
a animals home or
your ecomany.

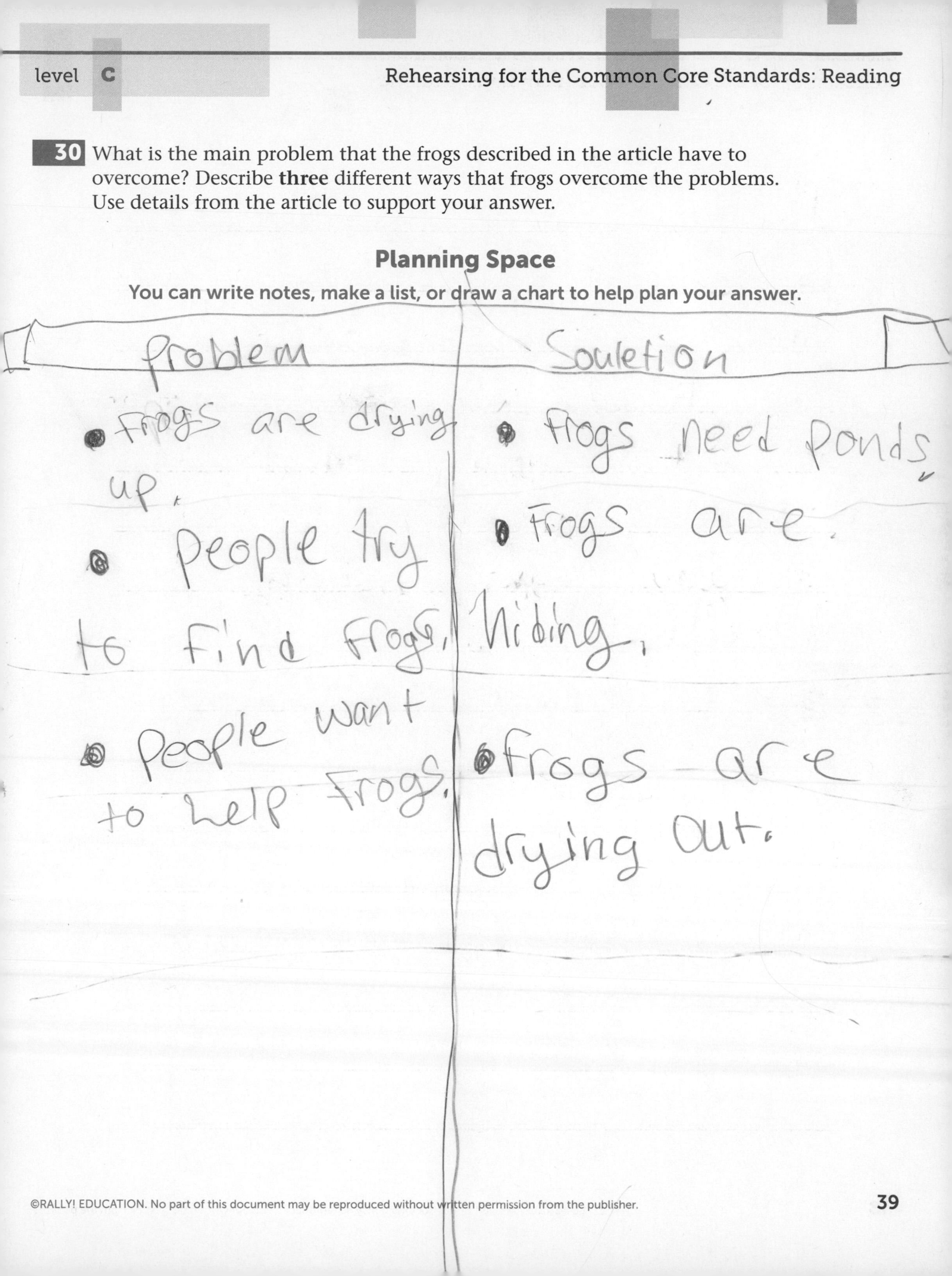

30 What is the main problem that the frogs described in the article have to overcome? Describe **three** different ways that frogs overcome the problems. Use details from the article to support your answer.

Planning Space

You can write notes, make a list, or draw a chart to help plan your answer.

Problem	Souletion
• Frogs are drying up.	• frogs need ponds
• people try to find frogs.	• Frogs are hiding.
• People want to help frogs.	• Frogs are drying out.

Directions: Read the passage. Then answer the questions that follow it.

The Squirrel and the Crow

An Indian Folktale Retold by Reena I. Puri

1 Once upon a time a crow and a squirrel owned a field. They agreed to work the field together. The crow built his nest in a tree near the field. The squirrel made her home in the trunk of the same tree.

2 One day the squirrel called out to the crow, "Come, Brother Crow. It's time to plow the field." The crow was lazy. He stretched his left wing and his left leg, then said:

3 *"Sister dear, do go ahead.*
I will follow soon.
I'll eat this piece of buttered bread
And be with you by noon."

4 The squirrel plowed the field all day. Meanwhile, the crow enjoyed the cool breeze that blew through the tree.

5 A few days later, the squirrel called out to the crow, "Come, Brother Crow. It is time to plant the seeds." The crow opened one eye and said:

6 *"Sister dear, do go ahead.*
I will follow soon.
I'll eat this piece of buttered bread
And be with you by noon."

7 The little squirrel planted seeds all by herself while the crow lay back watching the clouds.

8 Rain fell, and before long all the seeds had sprouted.

9 The squirrel called out to the crow once again. "Come, Brother Crow. It is time to hoe the weeds."

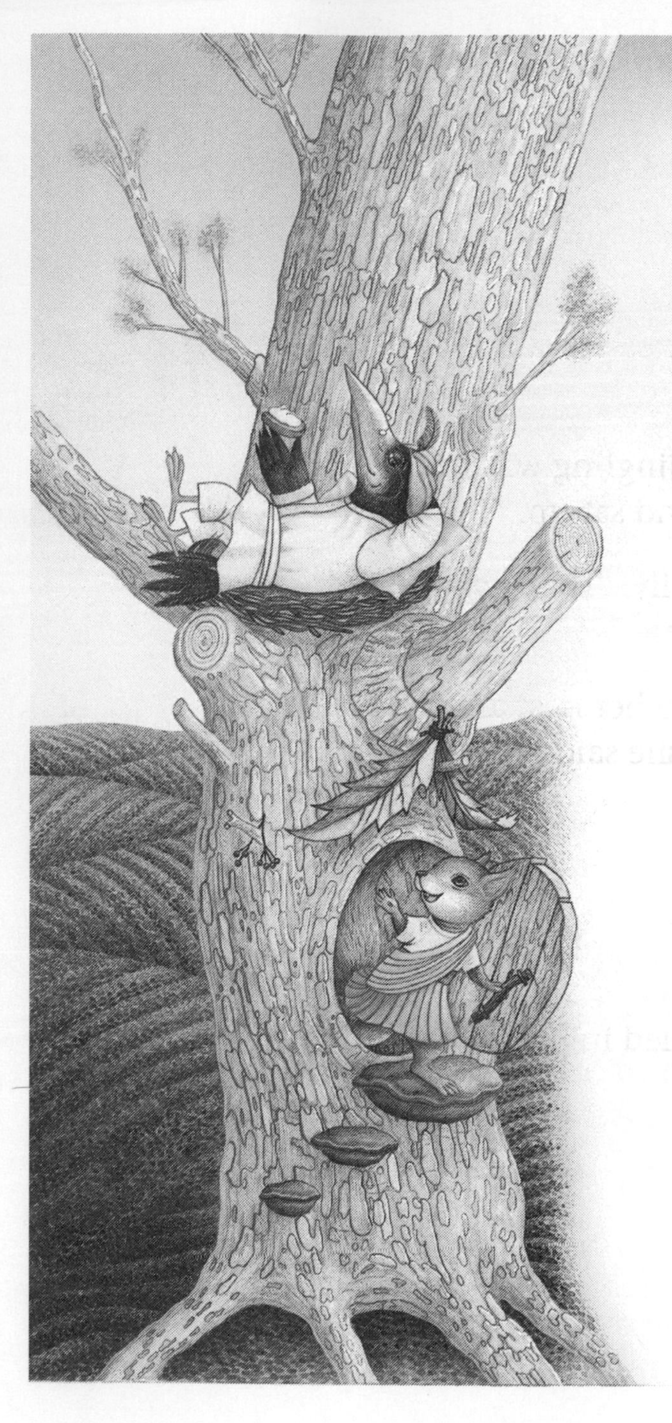

10 The crow slowly stretched his right wing and his right leg, then yawned.

11 *"Sister dear, do go ahead.*
I will follow soon.
I'll eat this piece of buttered bread
And be with you by noon."

12 The squirrel chopped down the weeds by herself.

13 The days passed. The sun shone brightly and helped the little plants grow big and strong. Before long every stalk had fat ears of wheat.

14 "Come, Brother Crow," called the squirrel. "It's time to harvest the grain." The crow settled himself in his nest, then said as usual:

15 *"Sister dear, do go ahead.*
I will follow soon.
I'll eat this piece of buttered bread
And be with you by noon."

16 The squirrel cut down the wheat. Then she separated the grains of wheat from the stems and husks. Soon there were piles of golden grain waiting to be put into sacks.

17 The squirrel mopped her brow with her bushy tail and called to the crow, "Come, Brother Crow, help me load the grain onto the cart and take it to the market."

18 The crow scratched his head with his foot, then answered:

19 *"Sister dear, do go ahead.*
I will follow soon.
I'll eat this piece of buttered bread
And be with you by noon."

20 The squirrel took the grain to the market. It was very good grain, and she sold it for a very good price.

21 She came home with a big silken bag jingling with money. The crow heard the sound of the money and sat up.

22 "Come, Sister Squirrel," he called greedily. "Let us count and divide the money so I can take my share."

23 The little squirrel dropped the bag into her nest and turned to the crow. Smiling her sweetest smile, she said:

24 *"Brother Crow, there is no share*
For lazy birds like you.
When all your buttered bread is gone,
You'll wish you had worked, too."

25 The squirrel flicked her tail and vanished into her nest. The crow sat on his branch feeling very silly.

Directions: Answer the following questions. If you need more space to write an answer, write your answer on your own paper.

31 Read these sentences from paragraph 4.

> ***"The squirrel plowed the field all day. Meanwhile, the crow enjoyed the cool breeze that blew through the tree."***

What is the main purpose of these sentences?

A to explain why the crow chooses not to work

B to compare how the squirrel and the crow act

C to describe why the squirrel does not need help

D to show that the squirrel and the crow are working together

32 All of the following details show that "The Squirrel and the Crow" is a folktale EXCEPT

A it starts with the phrase "once upon a time"

B its two main characters are animals

C its main purpose is to teach a lesson

D it includes a character speaking in rhyme

33 Read this sentence from paragraph 7.

> ***"The little squirrel planted seeds all by herself while the crow lay back watching the clouds."***

What do the actions of the two characters show about what they are like? How does this sentence emphasize how different they are? Use specific details from the sentence to support your answer.

The Sentense Shows that they are alike because they are both doing Something & they are different becallse One is relaxing & the Other One is Working

34 The squirrel works the field so she can sell the wheat grain. Complete the chart below to show the steps taken to work the field.

The field is plowed.

↓

Plant the seeds

↓

hoe the weeds

↓

Chopp the weed

↓

The grain is taken to the market and sold.

35 Each time the squirrel asks the crow to help, he says he will be with her later. How do his actions before he says this help show that he is lazy? Give at least **two** specific examples in your answer.

He streches a leg & a wing of opened an eye, the passege said "One day squirrel called & yawns out to the crow once agin come Brother crow it's time to hoe the weeds.

36 The crow is given many chances to help the squirrel. How does this affect what you think of the crow's character? Use details from the story to support your answer.

This affects what I think because the crow is lazy and doesn't help and wants creadit or wants a share

the crow made no effort at all

37 At the end of the story, the crow asks for his share of the money. Why does the squirrel not share the money with the crow? Use at least two details from the story to support your answer.

Because he doesn't Do anything and he says he will be there at noon, & never come.

38 Do you feel that the crow has learned a lesson? Explain whether or not you think he will act differently next year. Use details from the story to support your answer.

I ~~think~~ Feel he learned a lesson because ~~the~~ Squirrel didn't give him a share for a reason. Because he didn't Work at all.

39 Each time the crow is asked to help, he is eating bread. How does this become important at the end of the story? Describe how eating bread now is related to planting wheat for the future. Use details from the story to support your answer.

Planning Space

You can write notes, make a list, or draw a chart to help plan your answer.

40 The main lesson of the story is about being willing to work. How does the ending of the story show that it is important to work hard? Compare how things work out for the squirrel and the crow in your answer. Use details from the story to support your answer.

Planning Space

You can complete the charts below to help plan your answer.

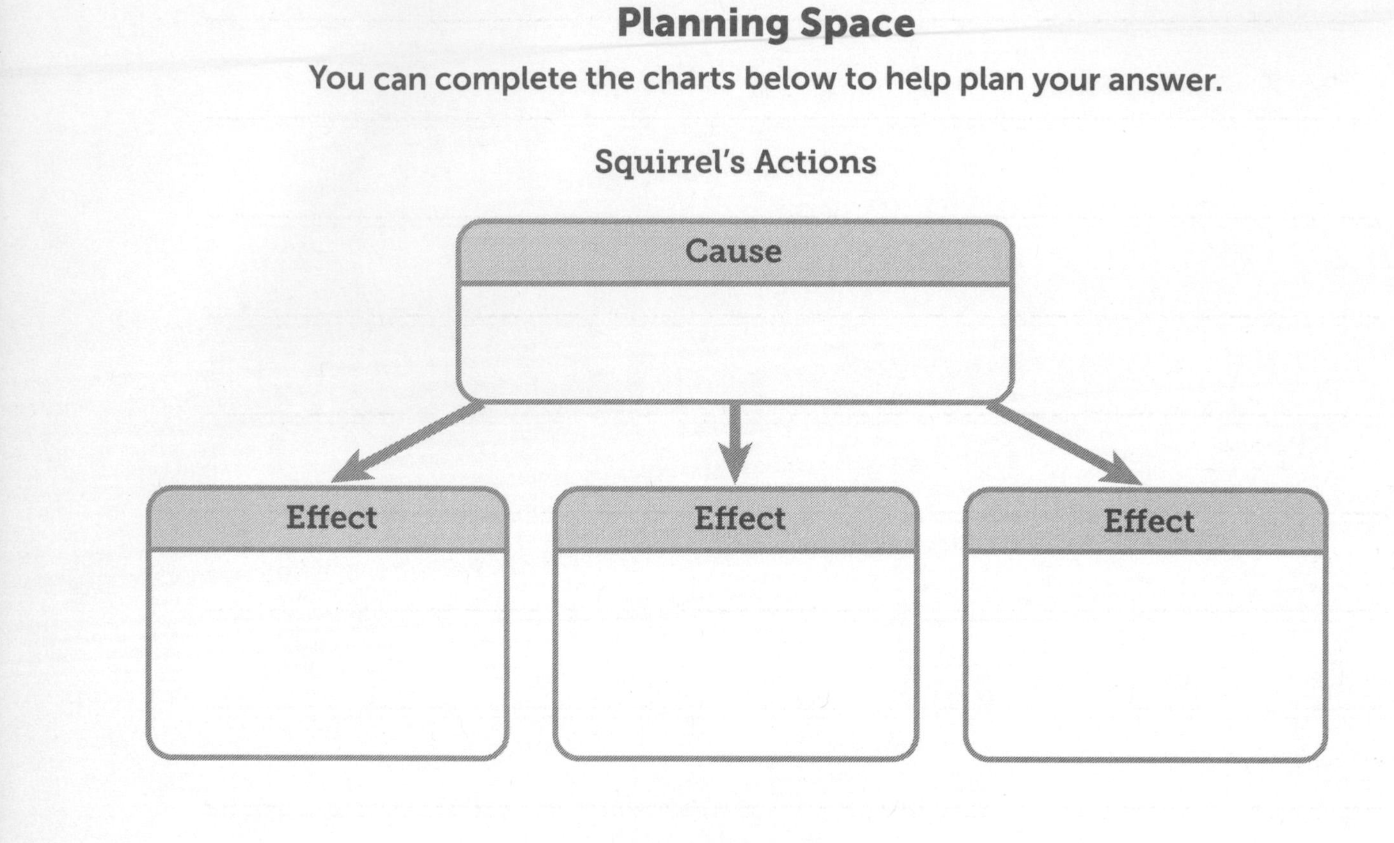

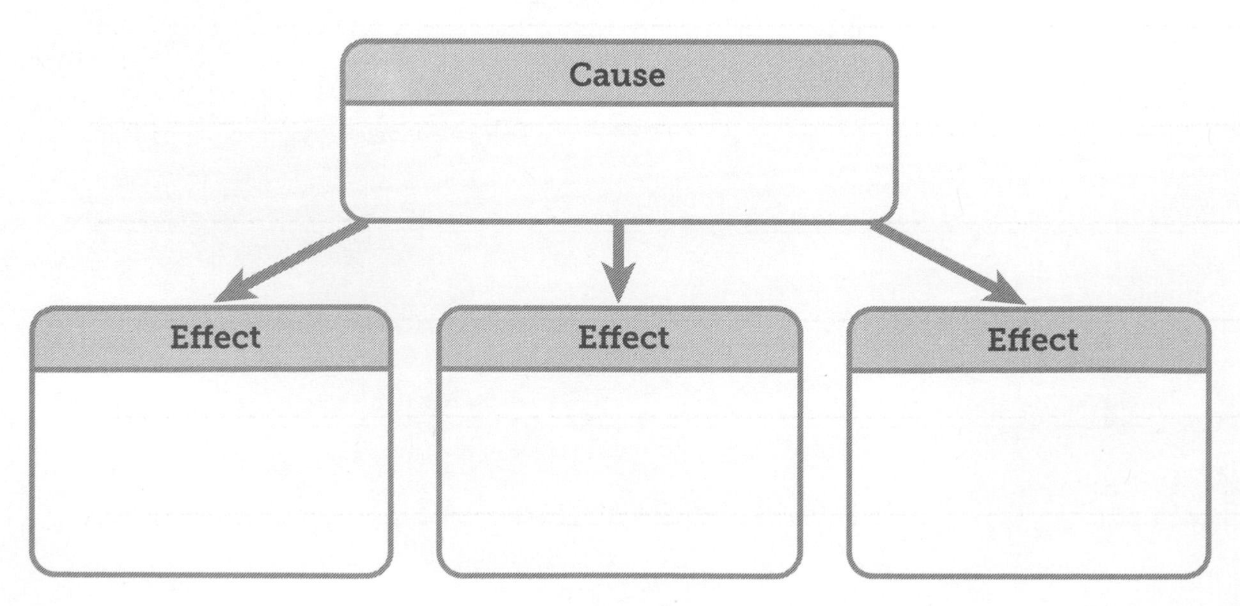

Directions: Read the passage. Then answer the questions that follow it.

Celebrating Raksha Bandhan

By Neelima Singhal

1 The bazaar is crowded this evening. It is the Hindu month of Shravan (August or September), in Delhi, India. People like to shop after the sun goes down during the hot summer months. I walk around the bazaar with my mummy, papa, and little brother, Sanjay. We are shopping for the festival of *Raksha Bandhan*, which is the full-moon day of Shravan.

2 *Raksha* means safety, and *bandhan* means bond. This special festival celebrates the loving and caring bond between sisters and brothers. A sister ties a *rakhi* to her brother's wrist as a request that he protect her in times of need. She is also wishing him a long and happy life.

3 Shopkeepers all around the bazaar display colorful rakhis. A rakhi is a silken cord decorated with beads, sequins, buttons, flowers, or paper cutouts. Sisters used to make rakhis at home, but now most girls buy them in the shops. There are so many to choose from! There are little ones to fit small boys and larger ones for men.

4 Salesmen shout to get our attention.

5 "*Didi, rakhi lo*" (Sister, pick a rakhi), calls one.

6 "*Sunder! Soonharri rakhi dekho*" (Look! Beautiful golden rakhis), calls another.

7 We walk into a small store on the corner. I see some simple rakhis. Then I see one that has tiny sequins and beads woven all over the red cord. It has little tassels on the end. I choose that rakhi.

8 On the day of the celebration, everyone gets up early and takes a bath. Sanjay and I wear new clothes, and Mummy prepares a special tray. On the tray she puts some red powder, a few grains of rice, fresh flowers, and Sanjay's favorite sweet.

9 When we are ready, Sanjay and I sit across from each other. I apply a small *tilak* (a dot made with red powder) on his forehead. I throw some grains of rice and a few flower petals on him. These are traditional symbols of good luck. I say a little prayer. And I feed him *laddu*, a flour-and-sugar ball filled with nuts, coconut, and raisins.

10 Sanjay then performs his role in the celebration. He puts a small gift on the tray, perhaps *rupees* (Indian money) or jewelry. By letting me tie a rakhi on his wrist, he pledges always to take care of me.

11 In ancient times, legends say, women would tie rakhis to the wrists of men leaving for battle and say a prayer that the men would return safely. When they came home, the men would protect those women.

12 This year, the festival of Raksha Bandhan will be celebrated on August 19. When sisters and brothers live apart, the sister mails a rakhi to her brother along with a greeting card. The brother responds with a gift. Raksha Bandhan is a special day when sisters and brothers think fondly of each other and pray for each other's blessings.

Make a Rakhi for Your Brother or Friend

By Connie Colón

1. Slide beads to the center of a piece of cord.
2. If you'd like, spell out a name with alphabet beads or sew a pompom to the center.
3. Tie a knot on each side to keep the beads in place.

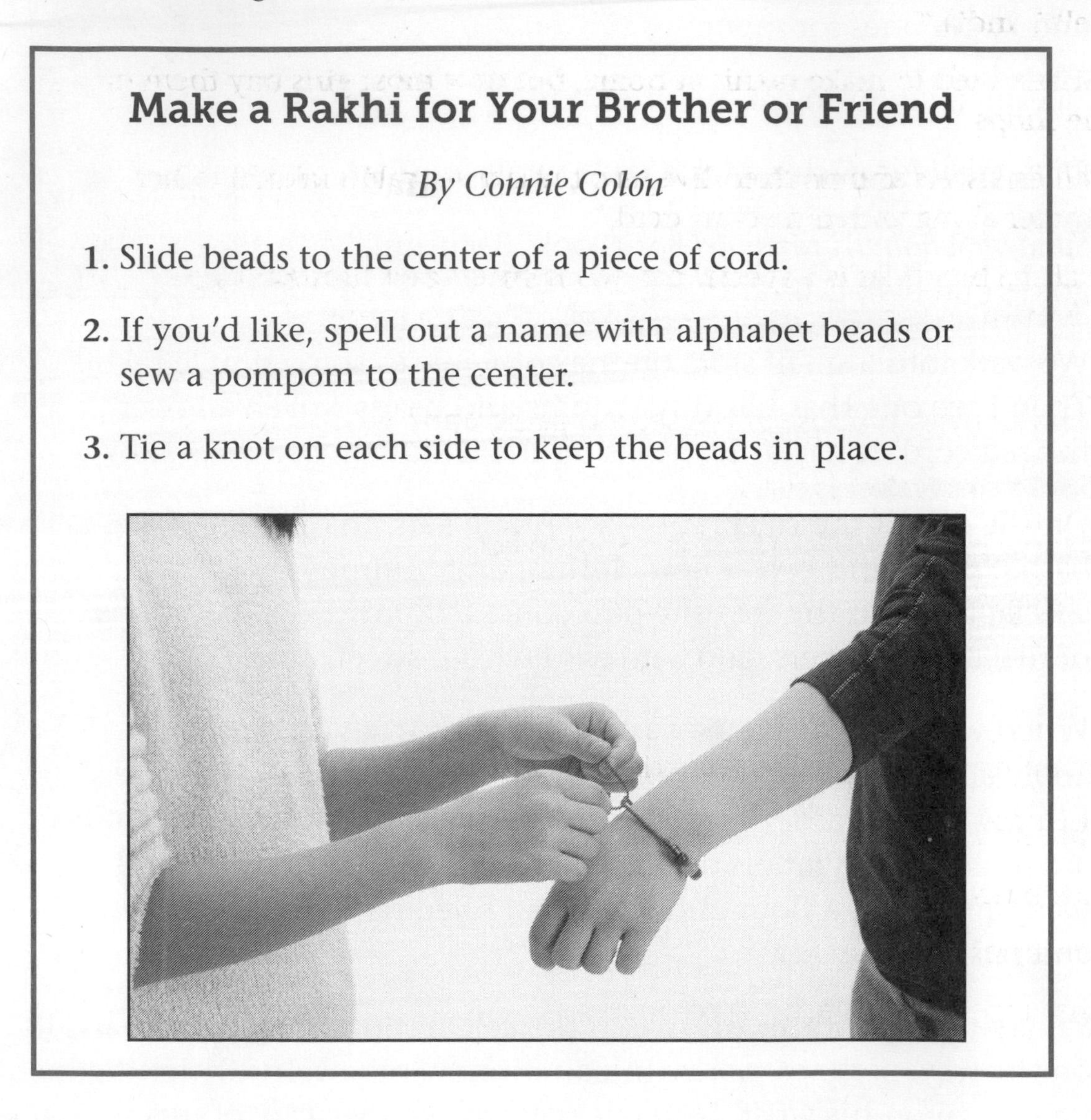

Directions: Answer the following questions. If you need more space to write an answer, write your answer on your own paper.

41 Which sentence states the main idea of the article?

A "It is the Hindu month of Shravan (August or September), in Delhi, India."

B "Sisters used to make rakhis at home, but now most girls buy them in the shops."

C "When sisters and brothers live apart, the sister mails a rakhi to her brother along with a greeting card."

D "Raksha Bandhan is a special day when sisters and brothers think fondly of each other and pray for each other's blessings."

42 What is the main purpose of the second paragraph?

A to tell how a rakhi is made

B to show how brothers and sisters should act

C to teach readers some Indian words

D to describe the meaning of the festival

43 The main feature that makes a rakhi special is

A what it means

B how much it costs

C how carefully it was made

D what type of beads are placed on it

44 Read this sentence from paragraph 2.

***"Raksha** means safety, and **bandhan** means bond."*

How does the meaning of the words summarize the meaning of the festival? What does the meaning show about the role of the brother? Use details from the article to support your answer.

This shows that the festival shows safety. This shows that the brother has to protect his sister when she is in need.

45 The author describes going to the bazaar. How does the description of the bazaar suggest that Raksha Bandhan is celebrated by many people in India? Use at least **two** specific details from the article to support your answer.

The author says that the bazaar was crowded. This means that a lot of people celebrate Raksha Bandhan.

46 The cord of rakhis can have many different items attached to it. Complete the web below by listing **six** items that can be added to the cord.

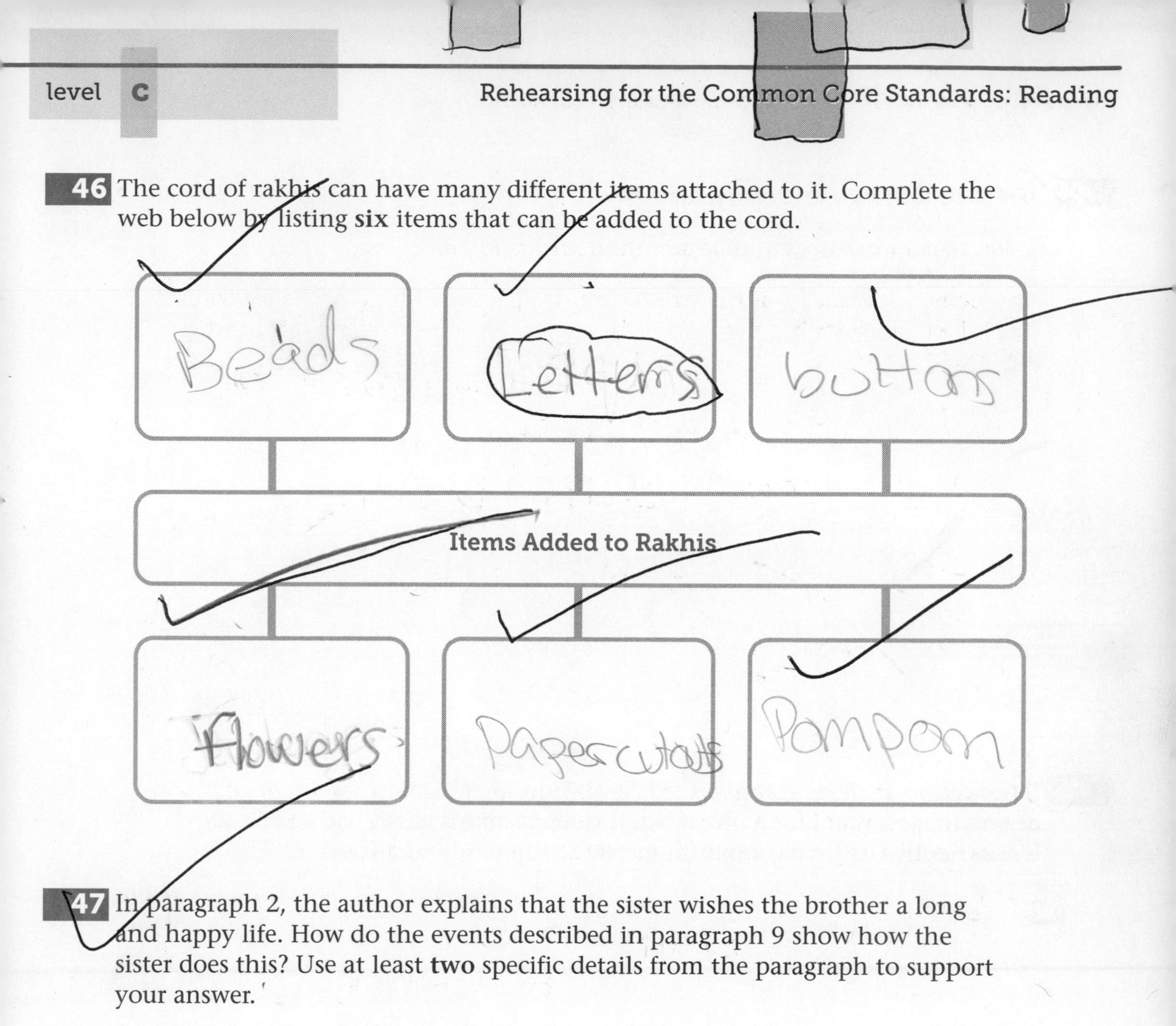

47 In paragraph 2, the author explains that the sister wishes the brother a long and happy life. How do the events described in paragraph 9 show how the sister does this? Use at least **two** specific details from the paragraph to support your answer.

The sister does this by doing Prayers Put a red dot on his Forhead and gives him laddu and him to always look after her.

48 Is the celebration of Raksha Bandhan important only to brothers and sisters or to the whole family? Explain why you feel that way. Use details from the article to support your answer.

This celebration is important to the whole family because the whole family might be Hindu I feel this way because I celebrate this to and even My aunt has to tie it on my Dad.

49 The section at the end is titled "Make a Rakhi for Your Brother or Friend." If you made a rakhi for a friend, what would it mean when you gave it to your friend? Use details from the article to support your answer.

It will mean good belesing And to live a long life or if to a friend it would mean long Friendship

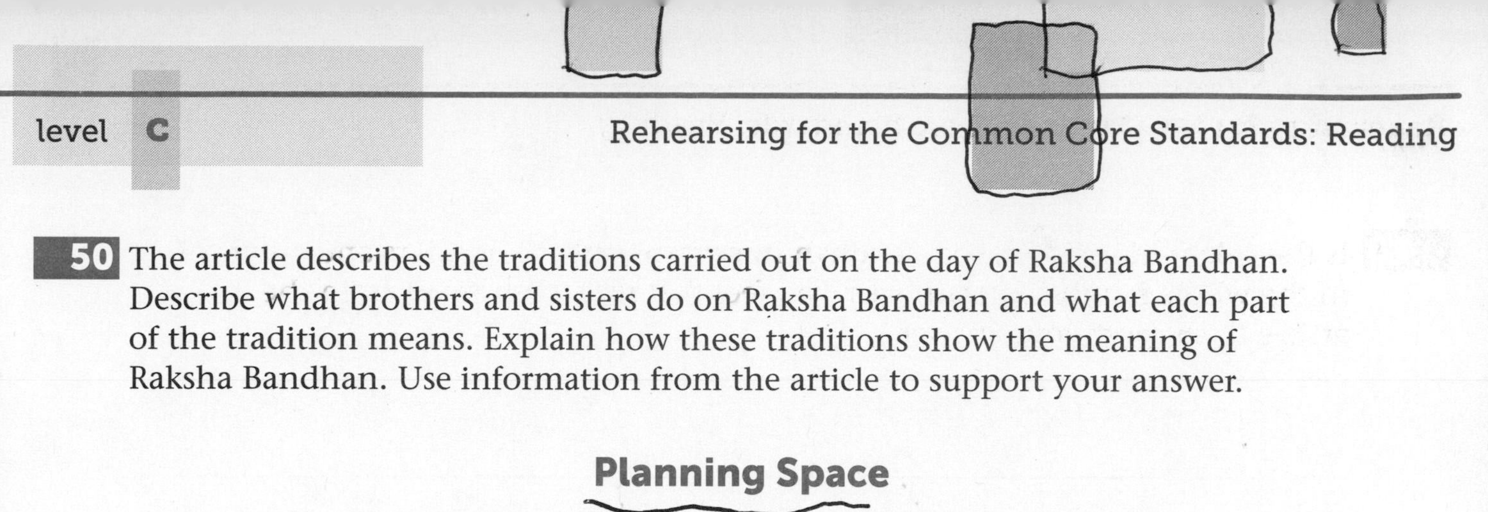

50 The article describes the traditions carried out on the day of Raksha Bandhan. Describe what brothers and sisters do on Raksha Bandhan and what each part of the tradition means. Explain how these traditions show the meaning of Raksha Bandhan. Use information from the article to support your answer.

Planning Space

You can complete the chart below to help plan your answer.

The Traditions Carried Out on Raksha Bandhan

Tradition	Meaning
Girls tie the bracelts on the Brothe	Girls hope a long life for thier brother
The brother puts Money or a gift.	For a thanx to the Sister.
Girls Do this to thier brother.	To Make sure the brother protects them.
The sister has to feed him laddu	To Make life sweet because laddu is sweet
the sister puts a tilak on her brother.	to show thier culture

Directions: Read the passage. Then answer the questions that follow it.

Fair and Square

By Eva Apelqvist

1 Hannah tightened the helmet strap under her chin. A man's voice boomed from the loudspeakers: "Participants in the Five-Mile Junior Fat-Tire Race, please gather behind the orange flags."

2 Hannah's stomach was churning. First prize was a mountain bike with clipless pedals and front suspension. On a bike like that, she'd fly through the woods.

3 "Good luck, junior mountain bikers," the loudspeaker voice boomed. "Three, two, one, and go!"

4 The lead-out, a man in a bright orange shirt with the words *Follow Me* printed on his back, started pedaling down the dirt road. The racers followed close behind.

5 Hannah squeezed her bike between a boy in a black spandex suit and a girl with a silver helmet. She passed a girl in a bright-green shirt. Four of them were up front now. Hannah was itching to take off, but she knew she wasn't allowed to pass the lead-out.

6 The lead-out made a turn onto a section of single track and gathered speed. A girl with a red braid rolled in behind him. Hannah pulled up behind the girl. The lead-out sped up again. Hannah downshifted for the incline, following close behind the girl with the braid, but the girl was gaining speed.

7 Curving around a pond, the course flattened. Hannah shifted up and pedaled the downhill section. Still, the braid girl biked faster. They crossed a wooden bridge. The lead-out and the girl disappeared behind a thick stand of trees. When Hannah glanced over her shoulder, she saw nobody behind her.

8 Hannah watched for the orange arrows marking the course and biked through the muddy fields. *The girl might still get tired,* she thought. Then Hannah saw her. At the edge of the forest, the girl was kneeling by her bike, the lead-out next to her. The girl must have gotten a flat. Hannah biked faster. She didn't shift down for the incline but pedaled harder. She wiped the sweat from her eyes, panting. The lead-out noticed her and jumped on his bike. Hannah was close enough now to see the girl putting the chain on the chain ring.

9 Hannah felt a jolt of energy as she followed the lead-out past the girl into the woods. Maybe she could win. On the uphill, she reached for her bottle and took a quick drink. She didn't have much water left, but they'd covered more than half the course.

10 In the middle of a small meadow, Hannah looked back. The girl was coming up behind her at a furious speed.

11 Hannah pedaled closer to the lead-out, who immediately pulled away. They entered the woods again, the lead-out now far ahead, disappearing around a bend. Hannah reached a fork in the trail. The lead-out was nowhere in sight, but there, to her left, was the sign with the orange arrow. When she turned, her foot slipped off the pedal, and she accidentally kicked the sign over.

12 *I need to stop and fix the sign,* she thought. *The other racers might get lost.* But even as she was thinking this, her feet kept moving faster, faster.

13 As Hannah entered the double track, she looked behind her, but the girl wasn't there.

14 "Hannah Anderson, winner of the Five-Mile Junior Fat-Tire Race!" the man on the loudspeakers announced as she passed the finish line.

15 "Hey!"

16 Hannah turned and saw the girl with the braid jumping off her bike.

17 "Good job," the girl called to Hannah, panting. "I thought I almost had you, but I must have missed a trail marker."

18 "You would have won if it hadn't been for your bike chain and getting lost," Hannah mumbled.

19 The girl was smiling. "No," she said. "It's all part of racing. You won fair and square."

20 Hannah swallowed hard. The girl's bike was rusty. No wonder her chain had jumped.

21 Leading her new bike away after the award ceremony, Hannah felt like crying. She looked around for the girl with the braid and found her by the water stand.

22 "I accidentally kicked the sign over," Hannah said softly.

23 The girl was quiet.

24 "You know, at the fork in the trail. I tipped the sign," Hannah said, a little louder. "I want you to have the bike."

25 As she handed over the bike to the shocked girl, Hannah felt the lump in her throat disappear.

26 "Are you sure ...?" the girl asked.

27 Hannah nodded. "I'm sure," she said.

28 The girl was beaming now, her finger moving along the shiny blue frame.

29 "Are you racing in Copper Harbor next weekend?" she asked. "I am."

30 Hannah grinned. "Yes," she said. "Let's see who wins then. Fair and square."

Directions: Answer the following questions. If you need more space to write an answer, write your answer on your own paper.

51 Which statement describes the main lesson that Hannah learns?

A Winning by cheating does not feel like a win.

B There is always someone better than you are.

C A good sportsperson needs the right equipment.

D The best thing you can win in life is a friend.

52 What does the girl's dialogue in paragraphs 17 and 19 show about her?

A She knows that Hannah cheated.

B She wanted to win the bike.

C She is mad at herself for losing.

D She is a good sport.

53 How does the girl with the braid getting a flat affect the events of the race?

A It causes the girl to give up on winning.

B It allows Hannah to get in front of the girl.

C It makes the lead-out lose his way.

D It changes the course the riders take.

54 Read paragraph 2 of the story. Explain how Hannah feels and why she feels that way. Use details from the paragraph to support your answer.

55 After Hannah kicks the sign over, the girl with the braid misses the turn. Did Hannah kick the sign over on purpose so this would happen? Use details from the story to support your conclusion.

56 Paragraph 12 tells Hannah's thoughts and Hannah's actions. Explain how her actions are different from her thoughts. What does this show about why she does not fix the sign? Use details from the paragraph to support your answer.

57 In paragraphs 15 to 20, Hannah talks to the girl with the braid. How does Hannah meeting the girl make her feel worse about what she did? Give at least **two** reasons Hannah feels worse in your answer.

58 Read this sentence from paragraph 25.

> ***"As she handed over the bike to the shocked girl, Hannah felt the lump in her throat disappear."***

What does this sentence show about how Hannah feels about giving away the bike? Explain why Hannah feels this way. Use details from the story to support your answer.

59 The title of the story is "Fair and Square." Explain how this title summarizes the main theme of the story. Use details from the story to support your answer.

60 At the end of the story, Hannah gives the girl with the braid the bike she won. Do you feel that Hannah did the right thing by giving the bike away, or should she have kept it? Explain why you feel that way. Use information from the story to support your answer.

Planning Space

You can complete the graphic organizer below to help plan your answer.

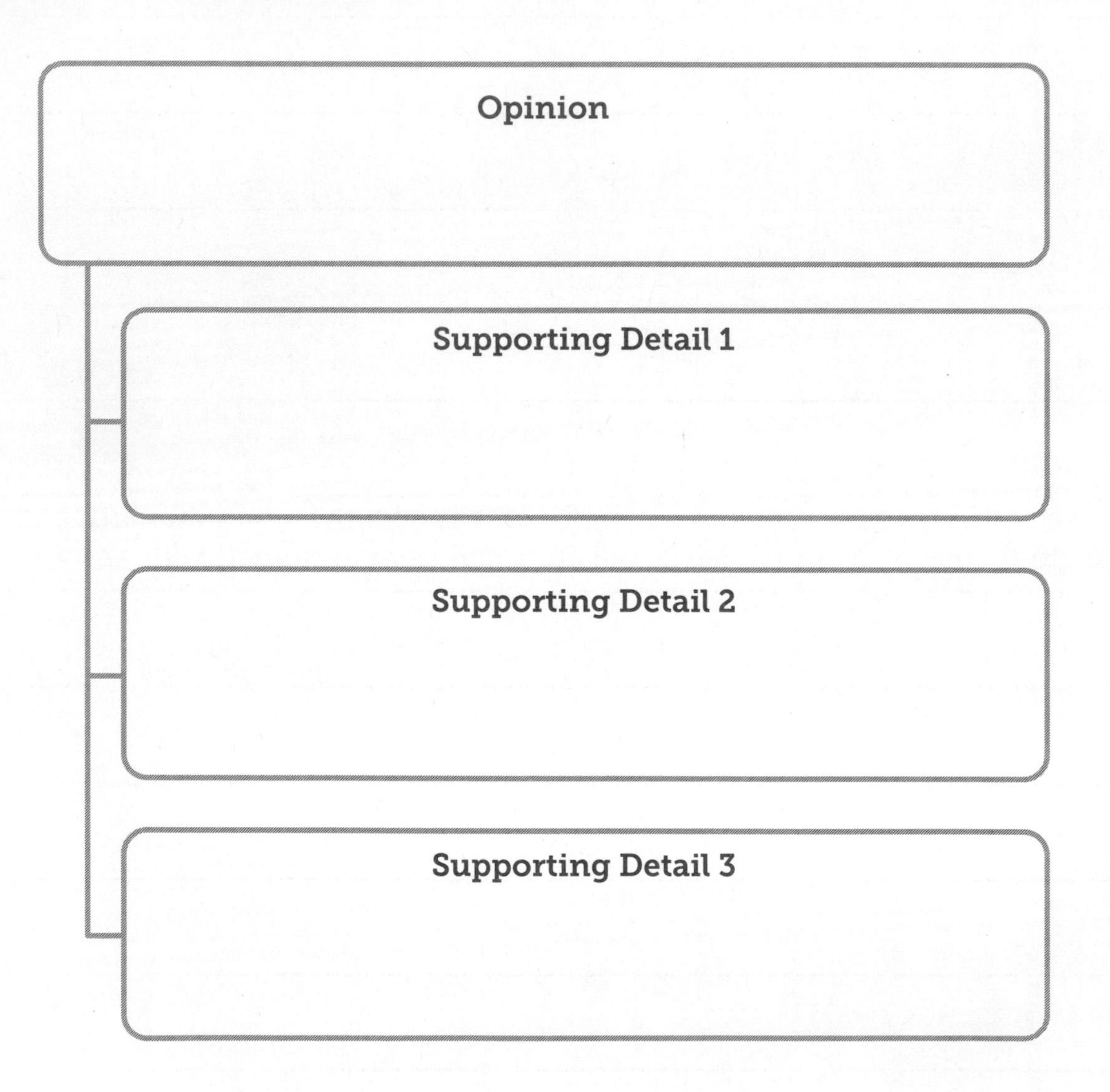

Part B:

Craft and Structure

Literary and Informational Passages with Multiple Choice, Short Response, Extended Response, and Essay Questions

Common Core State Standards for Informational Text (Grade 3)

RI.3.4 Determine the meaning of general academic and domain-specific words and phrases in a text relevant to a grade 3 topic or subject area.

RI.3.5 Use text features and search tools (e.g., key words, sidebars, hyperlinks) to locate information relevant to a given topic efficiently.

RI.3.6 Distinguish their own point of view from that of the author of a text.

Common Core State Standards for Literary Text (Grade 3)

RL.3.4 Determine the meaning of words and phrases as they are used in a text, distinguishing literal from nonliteral language.

RL.3.5 Refer to parts of stories, dramas, and poems when writing or speaking about a text, using terms such as *chapter*, *scene*, and *stanza*; describe how each successive part builds on earlier sections.

RL.3.6 Distinguish their own point of view from that of the narrator or those of the characters.

Directions: Read the passage. Then answer the questions that follow it.

Talent Night

By Annie Gage

1 Let me introduce myself: Benjamin Belinski, Human Talent Void.

2 Kate can make anything using origami. Tommy creates breathtaking beats on overturned plastic buckets. Olivia trained her miniature poodle to do tricks. And those are just my friends. My grade also boasts four dancers, a gymnast, two bakers, an aikido expert, six singers, and five artists, among others.

3 Every day my teacher asks if I've decided what to do. And every day I remind her that I have no talents.

4 "Nonsense, Benjamin," she says. "You'll think of something."

5 "I'll just have to be sick the day of the show," I announce to my friends one afternoon. "If you get a cold, be sure to cough on me."

6 "You must have a talent," says Kate. "Let's make a list. What are you good at?"

7 "Eating," I answer. "Watching TV."

8 Kate rolls her eyes. "Benjamin, be serious."

9 "Tormenting my little brother."

10 "You exasperate me." Kate looks at our friends. "Come on, guys. What are Benjamin's talents?"

11 "He's good with dogs," says Olivia. "My dog adores him."

12 "Oh, great," I say. "I can sit on the stage while he licks my face. Benjamin Belinski, Human Dog Toy."

13 "Benjamin's funny when he's sarcastic," says Tommy. He turns to me. "You could do a comedy routine."

14 "Yeah. Every joke could be about how I have no talents," I say.

15 "Benjamin," says Kate, "maybe you don't know how to juggle, but your birthday parties are the best."

16 "Yeah," agrees Olivia, "and you always get us together to do stuff. Like having game nights or riding bikes after school—or when we held that yard sale. The week you had the flu we didn't do anything fun."

17 "You're like the glue that holds us together," adds Tommy.

18 "Oh, great," I say. "Benjamin Belinski, Human Glue Gun."

19 But their comments get me thinking.

20 Lying in bed that night, I come up with a plan so exciting that it takes me two hours to fall asleep.

21 In the morning, I can't wait to tell my teacher. I zoom past my friends huddled together on the playground and run into the classroom.

22 "That's a marvelous idea, Benjamin," she says. "Resourceful, original, and true to who you are."

23 In the next few weeks, I write a zillion lists, make sure every item gets checked off, and ask a lot of people to do jobs. Kate agrees to make twelve origami centerpieces. I ask a variety store to donate lanterns. I get the principal's permission to cover the school's tables with blue and yellow paper.

24 On the night of the big event, I feel so nervous I have to force myself to eat dinner.

25 "The gym looks magical," my teacher says.

26 "This place has been completely transformed," I hear one visitor whisper.

27 When the show begins, each person with an act knows his or her place in the lineup. Tommy wows us with his drumming. The singers stay in tune throughout their songs. The gymnast astonishes us with handsprings and back walkovers.

28 During intermission, our guests smack their lips over student-baked cookies as they browse the display of paintings, drawings, pottery, and other artwork.

29 After the last act, performers gather for a final curtain call. My teacher steps onto the stage as the applause dies down.

30 "Everybody contributed and cooperated to put together this marvelous night," she announces. "However, one person deserves special recognition for taking the reins to make it proceed so smoothly. He stayed behind the scenes, but please give a big hand to an enormous talent—Benjamin Belinski, Producer!" She points to me in the back of the gym.

31 "Bravo!" the audience shouts. People turn to see who I am.

32 I wave sheepishly until someone grabs my arm and sticks my hand into the air to make me more noticeable. I bow.

33 Benjamin Belinski, Producer. I like the sound of that.

Directions: Answer the following questions. If you need more space to write an answer, write your answer on your own paper.

61 In which sentence does the narrator use exaggeration to make a point?

- **A** "Lying in bed that night, I come up with a plan so exciting that it takes me two hours to fall asleep."
- **B** "I zoom past my friends huddled together on the playground and run into the classroom."
- **C** "In the next few weeks, I write a zillion lists, make sure every item gets checked off, and ask a lot of people to do jobs."
- **D** "On the night of the big event, I feel so nervous I have to force myself to eat dinner."

62 Read this sentence spoken by the teacher at the end of the story.

> ***"However, one person deserves special recognition for taking the reins to make it proceed so smoothly."***

What does the phrase "taking the reins" mean?

- **A** making a mistake
- **B** picking people up
- **C** collecting the money
- **D** being in charge

63 In the first sentence, Benjamin describes himself as a "Human Talent Void." What does Benjamin mean by this? How does this introduce the main problem? Use details from the story to support your answer.

64 In paragraph 2, Benjamin gives details about his friends. Explain the purpose of giving these details. How do they help show how Benjamin feels compared to his friends? Use details from the story to support your answer.

65 Read these sentences from the story.

> ***"You must have a talent," says Kate. "Let's make a list. What are you good at?"***
>
> ***"Eating," I answer. "Watching TV."***
>
> ***Kate rolls her eyes. "Benjamin, be serious."***
>
> ***"Tormenting my little brother."***
>
> ***"You exasperate me." Kate looks at our friends. "Come on, guys. What are Benjamin's talents?"***

How do these sentences help show the meaning of the word *exasperate*? Use details from the sentences to support your answer.

66 At the start of the story, Benjamin's friends give him suggestions about what he could be good at. How does the way Benjamin responds show how he feels about the suggestions? Give at least **two** specific examples of what Benjamin says to support your answer.

67 Read this sentence from the story.

"You're like the glue that holds us together," adds Tommy.

Explain what Tommy means by this statement. Use details from the story to support your answer.

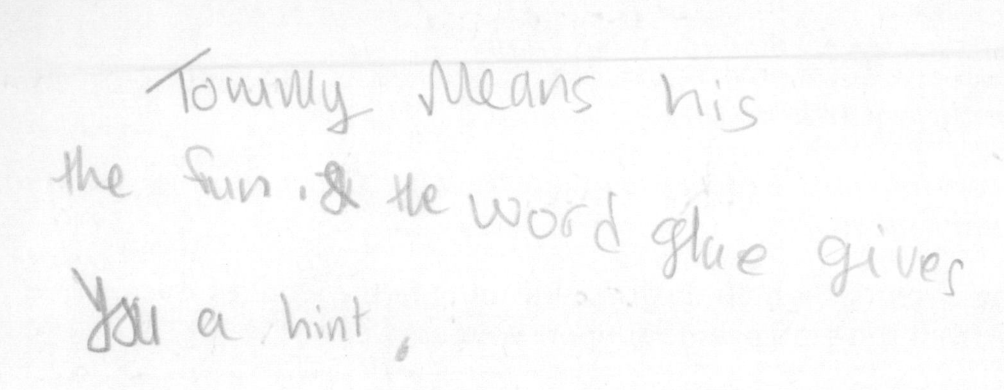

68 In paragraph 20, Benjamin describes how he has an idea. How is Benjamin's mood after he has the idea different from his mood before he has the idea? Use details from the story to support your answer.

His Mood befor was disapointed
Or dapressed.

69 After Benjamin has his idea, he is described carrying out the plan. However, the author does not show what the plan is until the end of the story. Explain why you think the author does this. Use details from the story to support your answer.

Planning Space

You can write notes, make a list, or draw a chart to help plan your answer.

I think the author does this because the authour wants a ~~[illegible]~~

- surpprise
- fanally
- happy ending

I think the author saved Benjurmen's idea for last because the auther wanted it to be a happy ending, surprise or even an fanally he wanted it to be between him and his teacher.

70 How does Benjamin feel about himself at the end of the story? What is the main way he has changed from the beginning of the story? Use details from the story to support your answer.

Planning Space

You can write notes, make a list, or draw a chart to help plan your answer.

Directions: Read the passage. Then answer the questions that follow it.

What Are the Birds Eating?

By Tony Helies

1 It's Memorial Day weekend, and I am sitting on a beach on Long Island, New York. A flock of small gray-brown shorebirds soars in and lands. The sanderlings are back, stopping off on their journey north.

2 Sanderlings spend the winter on the coasts of South America and the southern United States. When spring comes, they migrate as many as 6,000 miles to the Canadian Arctic, where they build their nests and raise their babies.

In spring, sanderlings stop on a Long Island beach during their journey to the Arctic. They are thin and hungry from their long flight.

Fuel Up!

3 It takes a lot of energy to fly thousands of miles. In the winter, sanderlings spend most of their time eating, and they turn that food into fat to give them energy for their long flight. By the time they reach Long Island, they need to refuel. They will stay on this beach for about three weeks, eating, eating, eating.

4 The sanderlings pause to look around. Then they start running along the shore, probing the sand with their beaks. As each wave rushes in, they dash up the beach just ahead of the water's foamy grasp. When the water recedes, they chase after it, stabbing at the sand as they run.

5 What are the birds eating, I wonder? After the birds move farther down the beach, I walk to the water's edge, squat down, and stare at the sand. I dig my hand in, pull up a clump of wet sand, and examine it closely.

6 At first I see nothing but sand, but then my eye catches something in motion. Carefully, I spread the sand across my hand. A gray dot scoots across my palm and disappears into a clump of sand. A little digging and I have him—a tiny mole crab. He has a rounded back and squirmy little legs. He is no bigger than a grain of rice. Maybe the sanderlings are eating mole crabs.

7 I bring a bucket to the shore and fill it up. Sorting through the sand, I count the mole crabs in the bucket. It is hard work because the crabs are fast, and they are the color of the sand. But I catch them one by one.

8 I find five large mole crabs—some as big as one inch long—and almost 200 little ones! When I return the crabs to the water, they disappear into the sand in seconds.

9 Later, the sanderlings return, eating their way along the beach. Most of what they are eating is small enough to swallow in one bite, so I can't see what it is. But then I see a bird pull out a mole crab that is too big to swallow whole. The bird drops it, pecks at it, and eats it in several bites. So the sanderlings are eating mole crabs.

A World of Creatures

10 Then I wonder, what are the mole crabs eating? Whatever it is, it must be really small. I bring some wet sand home and look at it under my microscope. I can see that the sand grains are shining bits of stone. Among them, I find a world of creatures. A white worm slithers along. Tiny shrimplike animals shoot by. At higher magnification I see microscopic plants small enough to hide behind a human hair.

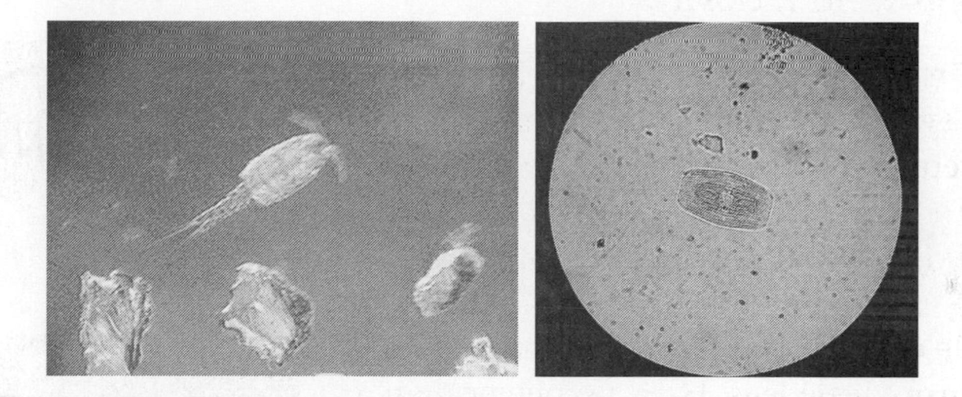

11 These microscopic animals and plants are all food for the mole crabs. When the mole crabs have a lot of food to eat, they have more baby mole crabs. That is a good thing for the sanderlings. Each sanderling needs to eat hundreds of mole crabs every day.

12 When the sanderlings arrive on Long Island, they may weigh two ounces. By the end of their stay, they can weigh almost twice as much. That's enough fuel, or fat, to take them to their next stop, the Arctic.

13 By mid-June, the sanderlings are gone, flying north, powered by mole crabs. But they will be back in August, stopping for lunch on their way back to their warm winter homes.

Directions: Answer the following questions. If you need more space to write an answer, write your answer on your own paper.

71 How did the author most likely feel while watching the sanderlings on the beach?

A worried

B amused

C curious

D annoyed

72 Read this sentence from the article.

> ***"Then they start running along the shore, probing the sand with their beaks."***

What does the word *probing* mean?

A breaking

B smelling

C eating

D searching

73 The sanderlings eat a lot during their time on Long Island. Explain why the sanderlings need to eat so much. Use at least **two** specific details from the article to support your answer.

74 One of the sections of the article has the heading "Fuel Up!" Explain why this is a good title for the section. Use details from the section to support your answer.

75 Read the caption of the photograph on page 85. Which detail from the caption shows that the birds have used up all their energy? Explain why you chose that detail. Use details from the article to support your answer.

76 The article describes what mole crabs are. Complete the chart below to summarize the information given on mole crabs.

Feature	Description
Size	
Color	
Body Shape	
Diet	

77 The section titled "A World of Creatures" describes the microscopic animals and plants. Explain what the word *microscopic* means. Use details from the section to support your answer.

78 Read these sentences from "A World of Creatures."

"A white worm slithers along. Tiny shrimplike animals shoot by."

How does the language used show how each animal moves differently? In your answer, identify the phrases used to describe the movement and explain what the words tell you about how the two animals move.

79 The author asks questions about what the sanderlings are eating and then about what the mole crabs are eating. Compare how the author answers each question. Include at least **one** similarity and **one** difference in your answer. Use details from the article to support your answer.

Planning Space

You can complete the chart below to help plan your answer.

How the Author Finds Out What the Animal Eats

	Sanderlings	Mole Crabs
What is studied?		
Where is it studied?		
How is it studied?		

80 The author describes the microscopic plants and animals in the sand. Why is it good for the sanderlings if there are many of these in the sand? Use details from the article to support your answer.

Planning Space

You can write notes, make a list, or draw a chart to help plan your answer.

Directions: Read the passage. Then answer the questions that follow it.

When Grandma Comes

By Eileen Spinelli

1 When Grandma comes, she likes to bring
a little bit of everything—
a puppy toy, some yellow thread,
a tasty square of gingerbread,
thick homemade soup, a knitted hat,
a can of tuna for the cat,
a couple pairs of woolen socks,
chocolate cherries in a box,
a picture book, a string of beads,
a bag of crunchy pumpkin seeds.

2 When Grandma comes, she likes to sing
And push me on the backyard swing.
And rock me in the rocking chair.
And read to me. And brush my hair.
She likes to dance me round the floor.
And walk me to the candy store.
And feed me soup by candlelight.
And tuck me into bed at night.

3 When Grandma comes, my parents grin.
The puppy barks. I laugh and spin.
The cat meows. The whole house hums.
On Saturday, when Grandma comes.

Directions: Answer the following questions. If you need more space to write an answer, write your answer on your own paper.

81 According to the poem, how often does Grandma visit?

A once each day

B once a week

C once a month

D once a year

82 Which statement describes the rhyme pattern in each stanza?

A Every second line rhymes.

B There are pairs of rhyming lines.

C The first and last lines rhyme.

D There is no regular rhyme pattern.

83 Who is the speaker in the poem? Explain how you can tell. Use details from the poem to support your answer.

84 Grandma can be described as thoughtful. Which stanza of the poem provides the best evidence to support this? Use at least **two** details from the stanza to support your answer.

85 The second stanza contains short sentences that often start with "And." What effect does this have on the feelings created by the poem? Use details from the poem to support your answer.

86 In the second stanza, the speaker describes many events. Explain how the events are ordered. Use details from the poem to support your answer.

87 Use details from the first and second stanza to complete the web below. Be sure to name the item and to include what the item is used for.

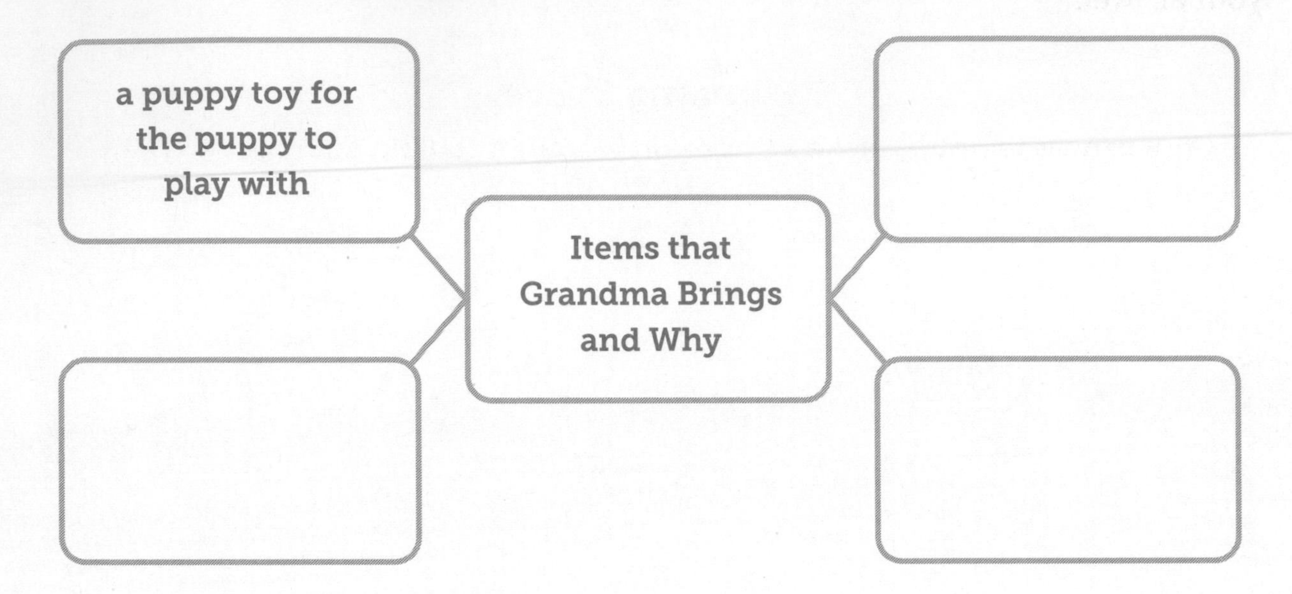

88 In the last stanza, the speaker describes how the "whole house hums." Explain what the speaker means by this statement. Use details from the poem to support your answer.

89 How do the details in the last stanza show how everyone feels about Grandma's visit? Use at least **three** details from the stanza to support your answer.

Planning Space

You can write notes, make a list, or draw a chart to help plan your answer.

90 Each stanza of the poem is about Grandma's visit. What is the main purpose of each stanza? Explain how the three stanzas fit together. Use details from the poem to support your answer.

Planning Space

You can complete the table below to help plan your answer.

Stanza	Purpose
First	
Second	
Third	

Directions: Read the passage. Then answer the questions that follow it.

Songs of the Sea

By Catherine Stier

1 You have signed on for months of hard work. You're far from home. The pay is bad. The food is worse. You find rare comfort in the simple songs that you and your work mates sing.

2 This is what a sailor's life was like in the 1800s. The songs sung aboard ships were called *sea shanties* (also spelled *chanteys*). You have probably heard a shanty or two yourself. Many of these songs have lasted through the years. They can often be found in surprising places today.

Sea Shanties Then ...

3 Sea shanties were valuable friends to sailors. Some shanties, such as "Blow the Man Down," had lively words and melodies. They broke up the boredom of long trips. Other shanties, including one called "Oh, Shenandoah," had a sadder tone. They helped seafarers express longing and loneliness. Still other shanties, such as "Leave Her, Johnny," let sailors grumble about their hard lives.

4 But the first job of the sea shanty was to help the men work as a team. Ships had sails that were controlled by a system of moving ropes. For many jobs, all of the sailors had to tug on the ropes at once.

5 When faced with such a job, the *shantyman*, or song leader, began a tune. The crew joined in on the chorus, and it might have sounded like a playful sing-along. But when the sailors came to a certain beat, they knew it was the signal to pull together with all of their might.

6 Raising or lowering the anchor called for a rhythm with a slow, steady motion. Then, the shantyman would choose a shanty with a slow, steady beat to match the job. Each duty on the sailing ship had its own rhythm and its own kind of song.

... and Sea Shanties Now

7 Sea shanties have been passed down to us in much the same way as folk stories. Long ago, someone came up with a memorable idea and melody. Others repeated the shanty, often adding changes along the way.

8 Over time, people saw the sea shanty for the treasure it was. Like any treasure, shanties were collected. Many were written down in books.

9 Where do the old shanties pop up now? Today's musical artists love the fun, beauty, and history of these songs. Many musicians, including Bob Dylan and Harry Belafonte, have their own versions of "Oh, Shenandoah." One group, the Robert Shaw Chorale, recorded a collection of shanties.

10 In Hollywood, shanties serve as a symbol of the sea. A fisherman sings the shanty "Spanish Ladies" in the film *Jaws*. The cartoon character Woody Woodpecker whistles "Blow the Man Down" when he finds himself aboard a pirate's ship.

11 Today, shanties tell us about shipboard life more than one hundred years ago. They help us understand what the working sailor sang and perhaps thought about.

12 So the next time you're doing a boring task, try making up a tune to go along with it. Time may pass more quickly, and your job may seem easier. Also, you may understand why sailors loved those old songs of the sea.

The shanty "Leave Her, Johnny" was often sung at the end of a trip. One of the last tasks before leaving the ship was to pump it dry. The shanty was sung while doing the task. The "her" referred to in the shanty is the ship.

Leave Her, Johnny

I thought I heard the skipper say,
Leave her, Johnny, leave her!
Tomorrow you will get your pay,
It's time for us to leave her.

The work was hard, the voyage was long,
Leave her, Johnny, leave her!
The seas were high, the gales were strong,
It's time for us to leave her.

The food was bad, the wages low,
Leave her, Johnny, leave her!
But now ashore again we'll go,
It's time for us to leave her.

The sails are furled, our work is done,
Leave her, Johnny, leave her!
And now on shore we'll have our fun,
It's time for us to leave her.

Directions: Answer the following questions. If you need more space to write an answer, write your answer on your own paper.

91 An assumption is a guess about something. In which sentence does the author make an assumption about the reader?

A "The songs sung aboard ships were called *sea shanties* (also spelled *chanteys*)."

B "You have probably heard a shanty or two yourself."

C "Today's musical artists love the fun, beauty, and history of these songs."

D "A fisherman sings the shanty 'Spanish Ladies' in the film *Jaws*."

92 Which paragraph in the section "... and Sea Shanties Now" best explains why shanties are described as treasures?

A Paragraph 9

B Paragraph 10

C Paragraph 11

D Paragraph 12

93 How does the first paragraph help readers imagine a sailor's feelings? Which use of shanties described in the article does this most help readers understand? Use details from the article to support your answer.

94 Describe the **four** ways that sea shanties helped sailors. Explain which use of the sea shanty was most important. Use details from the article to support your answer.

95 Read this sentence from "Sea Shanties Then ..."

> ***"Each duty on the sailing ship had its own rhythm and its own kind of song."***

What examples does the author give in the section to support this idea? Give **two** examples from the article in your answer.

96 Read paragraph 12 of the article. How does this paragraph help readers relate to the topic of the article? Use details from the article to support your answer.

97 In paragraph 3, the author describes sea shanties as "valuable friends to sailors." In what way were the sea shanties like friends? Use details from the article to support your answer.

98 The article includes two headings. How do the headings divide the information given? Describe how the main idea of each section is different. Use details from the article to support your answer.

99 The article describes how "Leave Her, Johnny" let sailors grumble about their lives. Use the words of the shanty to explain what the sailors grumbled about. Use at least **three** details from the shanty to support your answer.

Planning Space

You can write notes, make a list, or draw a chart to help plan your answer.

100 How has the purpose of sea shanties changed over time? Explain whether you feel that sea shanties today are as important as they were in the past. Use details from the article to support your answer.

Planning Space

You can complete the graphic organizers below to help plan your answer.

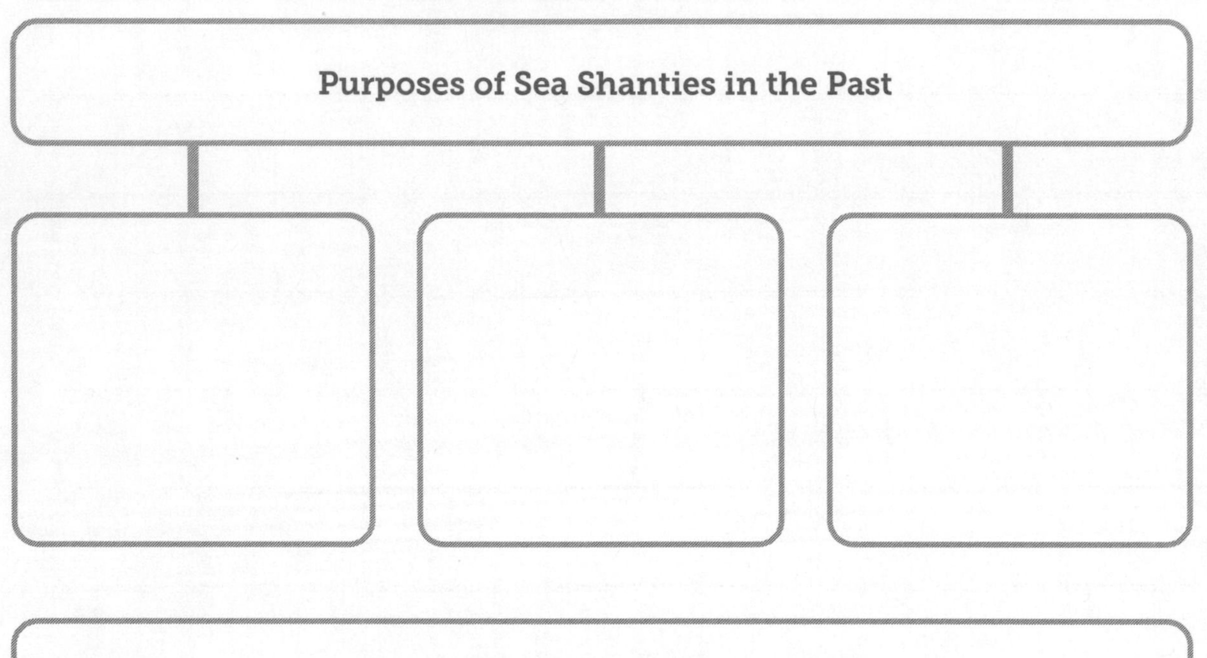

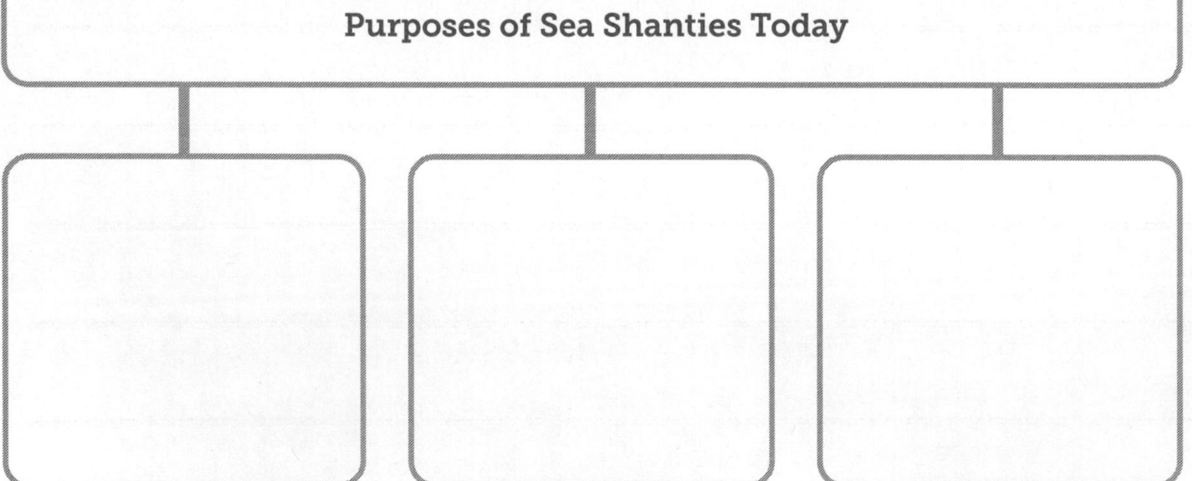

Directions: Read the passage. Then answer the questions that follow it.

Play Ball, Jaguar Paw!

By Chris Eboch

1 From the edge of the court, Jaguar Paw watched the older boys play a practice game of *pok-a-tok*. The ball moved around the court as players tried to keep it from touching the ground. They used their arms, knees, and hips, but never their hands or feet.

2 A player hit the ball with his hip and sent it flying. A boy from the other team swung his arm at the falling ball. *Smack!* The ball whizzed past the stone marker. A goal!

3 The scoring team cheered, and Jaguar Paw cheered, too. Someone ran after the ball, and the game resumed.

4 The ball sailed among the players, bouncing off the slanting stone walls along two sides of the court. A boy dove for the ball, his hair flying. He landed on his stomach, and the ball hopped out of the court.

5 "I got it!" Jaguar Paw yelled as the ball bounced toward him. He thrust his right hip forward, trying to knock the ball back into the court.

6 Instead, the ball slammed into his side. He fell to his knees and gasped for breath.

7 The players crowded around him, laughing. "Great move, kid!" someone said.

8 "Want to join our team?" asked the boy who'd missed the ball. "We could use someone like you—to make us laugh!"

Who Played Pok-a-tok?

Pok-a-tok was a ball game played by ancient Mayan people. The Mayan Empire reached its height between A.D. 300 and 900 in Mexico and the Central American countries of Guatemala, Belize, and Honduras.

9 Jaguar Paw couldn't believe that the player who'd just ended up on his stomach was making fun of *him*! But he couldn't think of anything clever to say.

10 Jaguar Paw trudged off the court and toward the market, trying to forget what had just happened. He gazed at fur-trimmed tunics, colorful caged birds, jade jewelry, and tasty-looking foods (cactus leaves, chili peppers, papayas, peanuts). Jaguar Paw especially liked the painted shields. He dreamed of his fourteenth birthday, when he'd get his warrior training. Then he could play ball and become a star.

11 Jaguar Paw left the market to head home. A *thunk-thunk-thunk* came from an alley. A boy his age was bending to pick up a pok-a-tok ball while a younger boy stood nearby, laughing. They had their own ball! Maybe they would let him play. He only needed a chance.

12 "Is it OK if I play, too?" he asked.

13 The boys looked at him. "Sure," they said.

14 "I'm Smoke Monkey," said the older one. "This is my brother, Scroll Bird."

15 "I'm Jaguar Paw. How should we do teams?" He hoped they wouldn't want to play together against him.

16 "How about if we just knock the ball around?" Smoke Monkey said. "Just for fun."

17 He tossed Jaguar Paw the ball. It was small, with a bumpy surface. It looked more like a big avocado than a pok-a-tok ball.

18 "All right," Jaguar Paw would practice with them. Then, when he became really good, he would find those other boys and prove himself. They'd ask him to join their team, and they wouldn't be joking.

19 He bounced the ball off his knee, knocking it against a wall. The ball bounced back, and Smoke Monkey hit it with his knee. Scroll Bird dashed forward and stopped the ball with his hip. It glanced off the wall, and Jaguar Paw swatted it with his arm.

20 Smoke Monkey slid onto his knees in the dirt, smacking the ball with his hip just before it touched the ground. As the ball sailed up, Scroll Bird reached out and whacked it, sending it straight at Jaguar Paw.

21 Jaguar Paw turned his hip toward the ball, but it sailed right past him, just brushing his backside.

22 He felt his face burn. He'd messed up again.

23 Scroll Bird ran to retrieve the ball. Smoke Monkey stood up, brushing dirt off his knees. "Nice try."

24 Jaguar Paw stared at him, wondering if that was a joke. Scroll Bird slid to a stop beside Jaguar Paw and held out the ball. "You start." Both brothers smiled. They *weren't* teasing him. They didn't care how well he did. They just wanted to play pok-a-tok.

25 Jaguar Paw looked at the ball. Could he really play just for fun and forget about being great? Smoke Monkey and Scroll Bird smiled, waiting for him to start.

26 Jaguar Paw grinned at his new friends, then tossed the ball up in the air.

Directions: Answer the following questions. If you need more space to write an answer, write your answer on your own paper.

101 Read these sentences from the first paragraph.

> ***"The ball moved around the court as players tried to keep it from touching the ground. They used their arms, knees, and hips, but never their hands or feet."***

What is the main purpose of these sentences?

A to tell the history of the game

B to show why Jaguar Paw wanted to play the game

C to describe how the game is played

D to suggest that the game could be dangerous

102 Which words in paragraph 2 are included to create a sense of speed?

A "swung his arm"

B "falling ball"

C "whizzed past"

D "stone marker"

103 In paragraph 25, what does the question asked represent?

A what Jaguar Paw is thinking

B what Jaguar Paw says to the boys

C what Smoke Monkey says to Scroll Bird

D what the author thinks Jaguar Paw should do

104 Read this sentence from paragraph 10.

"Jaguar Paw trudged off the court and toward the market, trying to forget what had just happened."

What does the word *trudged* suggest about how Jaguar Paw is walking? How does this detail help show how he feels? Use details from the story to support your answer.

The word "trudged" suggests that Jagur paw was walking well he was sad. It help shows how he feels because in the Passege he was upset.

105 Read the information in the section titled "Who Played Pok-a-tok?" Explain why the author included this information. What does it suggest about the setting of the story? Use details from the story to support your answer.

The autor inclued this because Maybe the reader wanted to know more about where this game came from & where it is played. This suggests on the setting maybe it was played alot long ago.

106 In paragraph 6, the author describes how Jaguar Paw is hit by the ball. Give **two** specific examples of ways the author emphasizes that Jaguar Paw is hit hard.

Jaguar Paw was on his knees. &

He was "trudged" well walking by the Market.

107 Paragraphs 7 and 8 describe how the players react when Jaguar Paw is hit by the ball. Do you feel that the boys are mean to Jaguar Paw? Use at least **two** details from the story to support your conclusion.

I feel they are mean because he was hurt and no one helped him & they were making fun of him.

108 The way the older boys make fun of Jaguar Paw affects his later actions. Complete the chart below by listing **two** ways the events with the older boys affect Jaguar Paw later in the story.

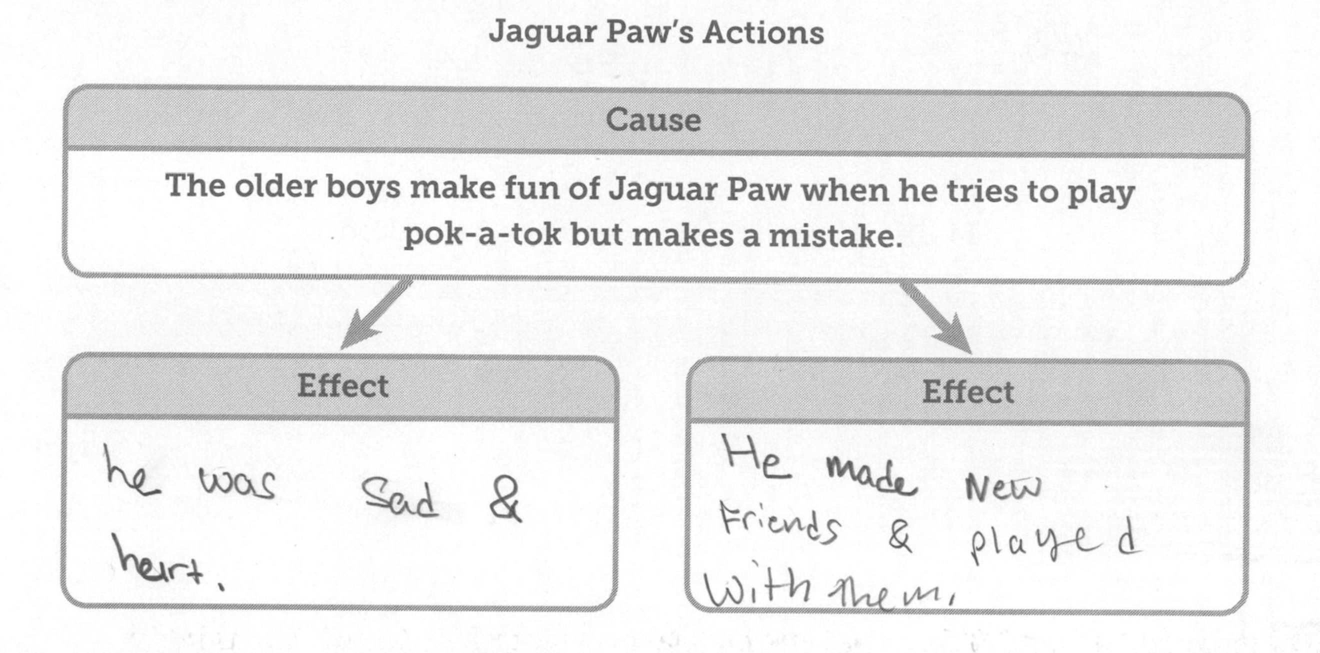

109 Read these sentences from paragraph 22.

"He felt his face burn. He'd messed up again."

What do these sentences suggest about how Jaguar Paw expects Smoke Monkey and Scroll Bird to react? Use details from the story to support your answer.

They ~~suggest~~ expects that Jacuar paw doesn't want to mess up in frout of his new friends. in case he mess up.

110 In the story, Jaguar Paw tries playing pok-a-tok with the older boys and plays pok-a-tok with Smoke Monkey and Scroll Bird. Describe **three** ways the two games are different. Explain what Jaguar Paw learns because of the differences. Use information from the story to support your answer.

Planning Space

You can complete the chart below to help plan your answer.

Main Differences Between the Two Games

Game with the Older Boys	Game with Smoke Monkey and Scroll Bird
1) Kids were falling or getting heart.	~~They were~~ just Playing for fun.
2) Making fun Of Jaguar Paw.	being friends with Jaguar Paw.
3) not playing for fun. (Competative)	Playing for fun.

Directions: Read the passage. Then answer the questions that follow it.

The World's Greatest Underachiever

By Henry Winkler

1 All through grade school, I was tutored. If I got a D, I was in heaven. If I got a C-minus, it was like I had achieved greatness. A's, B's, even C's were a kingdom that I never had a passport to. I studied my spelling words in my apartment in New York City. Somehow, during the time it took me to walk the block from my apartment to my school, the words vanished.

2 My teacher, Miss Adolf, had given me a list of ten spelling words. One of the words was *suburban*. One of the words was *neighbor*. One was *rhythm*. My mother and I went over the list until I knew those words. I felt terrific. I thought, *Wow! This time, I'm going to pass*. Finally, no extra study time, no detention, no being grounded.

3 The next day, I went into the classroom, sat down, and took out a sheet of loose-leaf paper. I dated it and wrote my name in the left-hand corner. I wrote the numbers down the left side on each line—1 through 10. Up until this point, I was getting 100 percent.

4 Then Miss Adolf gave us the words. They were not in the order that I had studied them, but that seemed OK. The first word was *carpet*. I wrote that one down: *c-a-r-p-e-t*. I was feeling pretty confident. Then came *neighbor*—I wrote down the letter *n*. Then *rhythm*—I knew there was an *r*. *Suburban*—I wrote *s-u-b*. My heart sank. I had gone from 100 percent to maybe a D-minus. Where did the words go?

5 I knocked my head. Were the words holding on to the side of my brain? Could I knock them into my pencil?

6 Some people talk about information sliding off the blackboard of your brain. That was my life. I was called "stupid," "lazy." I was told that I was not "living up to my potential." My self-image was down around my ankles.

7 The one thing I had going for me was my sense of humor. I was funny—the class clown. When the teacher read us a story, I would act it out. If someone was shooting ducks out of the air in the story, I'd get behind my chair and pretend that I was shooting ducks. That sure didn't get me any A's. It got me a trip downstairs to the principal's office. And that wasn't funny at all. No matter what I did, it didn't seem to make a difference.

8 I wish I'd known then what I know now: I have dyslexia. My brain learns differently. I didn't find that out until I was about thirty years old. My stepson, Jed, was in the third grade, and we had him tested for learning differences. As they explained dyslexia to him, I thought, *Oh, my goodness! That's me.*

9 A learning disability can really affect the way you feel about yourself. Now I know that even if a person learns differently, he or she can still be filled with greatness. Every one of us has something special inside. It's our job to figure out what that is. Dig deep, get it out, and give it to the world as a gift.

Henry Winkler starred as Arthur Fonzarelli, "The Fonz," in the popular television series Happy Days, *and has appeared in a number of films, including* Holes. *Along with acting, producing, and directing, Winkler is currently co-writing a series of books,* Hank Zipzer, the World's Best Underachiever. *He has just finished the sixth book in the series.*

Directions: Answer the following questions. If you need more space to write an answer, write your answer on your own paper.

111 In paragraph 2, why does Winkler feel good about the test?

A There are only ten words.

B The words are easier than usual.

C He has studied the words well.

D He only expects to get a D.

112 Winkler describes how he was told he was not "living up to his potential." What does this mean?

A He was not trying hard enough.

B He was not doing as well as he could have.

C He was not going to go very far in life.

D He was not making his teacher happy.

113 Based on Winkler's main problem, which type of work described in the last section is most important?

A acting

B producing

C directing

D writing

114 Read this sentence from the first paragraph.

> ***"A's, B's, even C's were a kingdom that I never had a passport to."***

Explain what Winkler means by this sentence. Use details from the article to support your answer.

115 Read paragraph 5 of the article. How do Winkler's actions and thoughts show how he feels? Use details from the paragraph to support your answer.

116 In paragraph 4, Winkler describes what he wrote down when spelling the four words. What do these details show about how hard he found spelling? Use details from the paragraph to support your answer.

117 In paragraph 9, Winkler has a message for the reader. What does Winkler want readers to know? Do you feel this is an important message? Use details from the article to support your answer.

118 Read this sentence from the article.

"A learning disability can really affect the way you feel about yourself."

How does Winkler support this statement? Use at least **two** details from the article in your answer.

119 The information at the end of the article describes Winkler's book series. Describe **two** details that suggest that the book series is based on his life. Use details from the article to support your answer.

120 Winkler did not learn that he had dyslexia until he was about thirty years old. How did not knowing he had dyslexia affect Winkler as a student? Describe how it affected his schoolwork and how he felt about himself. How might his time at school have been different if he had known he had dyslexia? Use information from the article to support your answer.

Planning Space

You can complete the chart below to help plan your answer.

How Dyslexia Affected Winkler

Effects on His Schoolwork	Effects on His Feelings

Part C:

Integration of Knowledge and Ideas

Literary, Informational, and Paired Passages with Multiple Choice, Short Response, Extended Response, and Essay Questions

Common Core State Standards for Informational Text (Grade 3)

RI.3.7 Use information gained from illustrations (e.g., maps, photographs) and the words in a text to demonstrate understanding of the text (e.g., where, when, why, and how key events occur).

RI.3.8 Describe the logical connection between particular sentences and paragraphs in a text (e.g., comparison, cause/effect, first/second/third in a sequence).

RI.3.9 Compare and contrast the most important points and key details presented in two texts on the same topic.

Common Core State Standards for Literary Text (Grade 3)

RL.3.7 Explain how specific aspects of a text's illustrations contribute to what is conveyed by the words in a story (e.g., create mood, emphasize aspects of a character or setting).

RL.3.8 (Not applicable to literature)

RL.3.9 Compare and contrast the themes, settings, and plots of stories written by the same author about the same or similar characters (e.g., in books from a series).

Directions: Read the passage. Then answer the questions that follow it.

Windmills Fixed the Floods!

By Carmen Bredeson

1 Hundreds of years ago, nearly half of Holland was covered with water. Much of the land was below sea level and was often flooded by the North Sea. This made the land swampy.

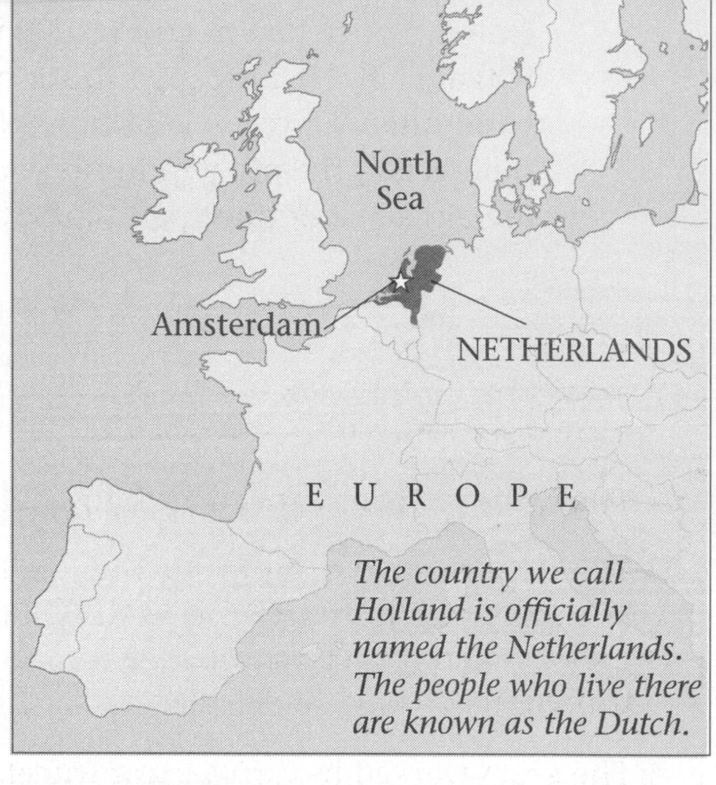

The country we call Holland is officially named the Netherlands. The people who live there are known as the Dutch.

2 Dutch people needed the land for farming. They began building dikes, which are huge walls of dirt. Dikes held back water from the North Sea. But farmers also needed a way to pump out the water that was already on the land.

3 Windmills were the answer. For hundreds of years, windmills had been in use all over the world. Some windmills ground grain into flour. Others sawed logs into lumber. During the 1400s and 1500s, the Dutch built windmills to pump water from the land. Luckily for them, Holland is very windy.

4 Thanks to windmills, fields that were once underwater were now dry. They could be used for crops. The drained fields were called *polders*.

5 Storms and floods brought more water to the land. Windmills kept turning to keep the fields dry.

6 In the 1800s, steam engines and electricity started powering the pumps that drained the fields. The new pumps would work even when it was not windy. Many of the windmills were torn down. Hundreds more were burned or destroyed in storms. Lightning struck many of the old wooden windmills because they were the tallest things in the fields.

7 Holland once had nearly 10,000 windmills. Today only about 900 are left. Historic organizations are trying to save the old windmills. Many are kept in working order. In case the modern pumps fail, the old windmills could be used again. Windmills remain an important part of the history and landscape of Holland.

1 Strong winds blowing off the North Sea turned the windmill's huge **blades**.

2 The blades were attached to a long **shaft**.

3 The shaft turned a **gear** inside the windmill. This gear's teeth fit into the teeth of more gears. When one gear turned, the others turned, too.

4 The gears worked to turn a **giant wheel**. The **scoops** on the wheel picked up water. The scoops went up in the air until they were at the top of the wheel.

5 As the scoops went over the top, they dumped water into a **channel** built higher than the ground.

The next windmill in line scooped up water and dumped it into an even higher channel. Finally, the water was dumped back into the sea.

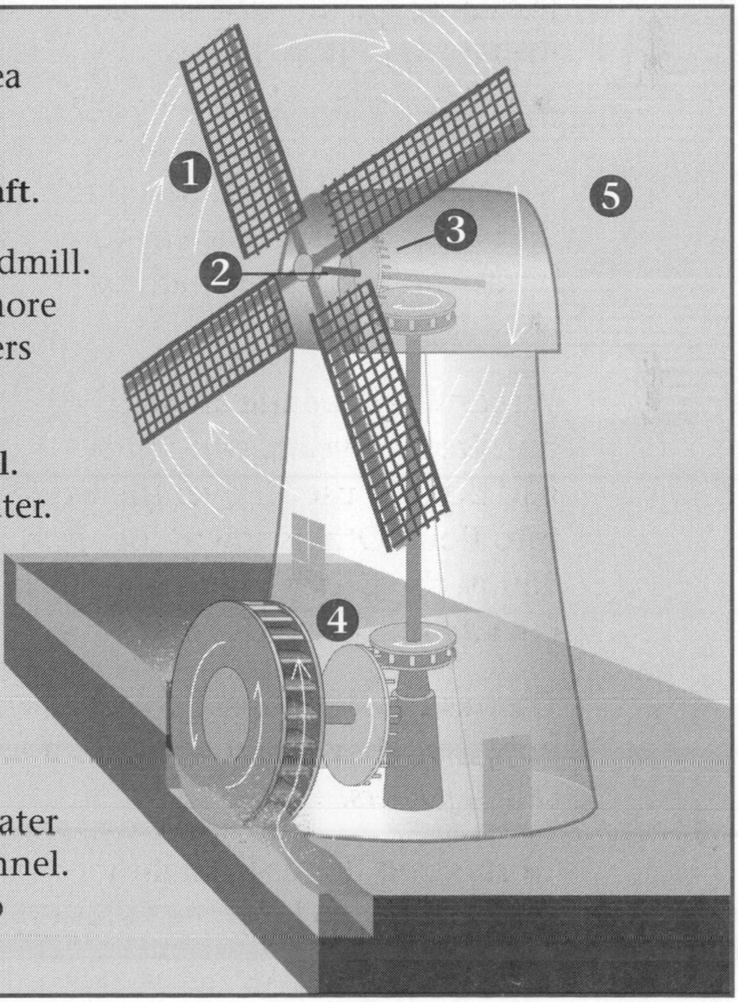

Directions: Answer the following questions. If you need more space to write an answer, write your answer on your own paper.

121 Which sentence best shows that building the windmills solved the main problem?

A "Dutch people needed the land for farming."

B "But farmers also needed a way to pump out the water that was already on the land."

C "For hundreds of years, windmills had been in use all over the world."

D "Thanks to windmills, fields that were once underwater were now dry."

122 Which feature about the Netherlands shown in the map is most important to the main idea of the article?

A It is a country in Europe.

B Its area is small.

C It borders the North Sea.

D Its capital is Amsterdam.

123 Look closely at the diagram of the windmill. What do the numbers on the windmill represent? How do they help readers understand the diagram? Use details from the diagram to support your answer.

124 The dikes were built to hold back water from the sea. Why were windmills still needed after the dikes were built? Use at least **two** details from the article to support your answer.

125 In what way did windmills change in the 1800s? Explain the main benefit of the change. Use details from the article to support your answer.

126 The article explains that there are now only about 900 out of 10,000 windmills left. Complete the web below by listing **three** more ways the windmills were destroyed.

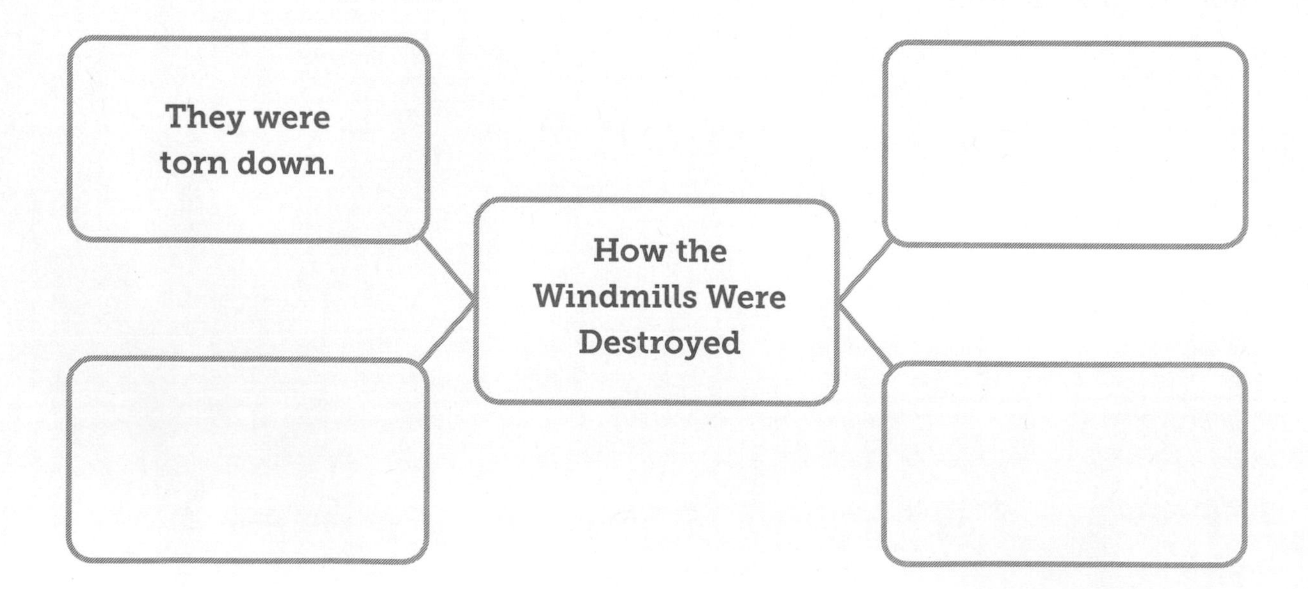

127 Describe the **two** reasons the author gives for saving the windmills. Which reason do you feel is most important? Explain why you feel that way. Use details from the article to support your answer.

128 Read paragraph 7 of the article. How is the purpose of this paragraph different from the purpose of the rest of the article? Use details from the article to support your answer.

129 Holland being on the coast caused the main problem, but it also helped solve the main problem. Explain how being on the coast both caused and helped solve the problem. Use details from the article to support your answer.

Planning Space

You can write notes, make a list, or draw a chart to help plan your answer.

130 The diagram shows how the windmills removed the water. Using the diagram as a guide, describe how the windmills worked. Tell how this helps explain why so many windmills were needed. Use details from the article and the diagram to support your answer.

Planning Space

You can complete the chart below to help plan your answer.

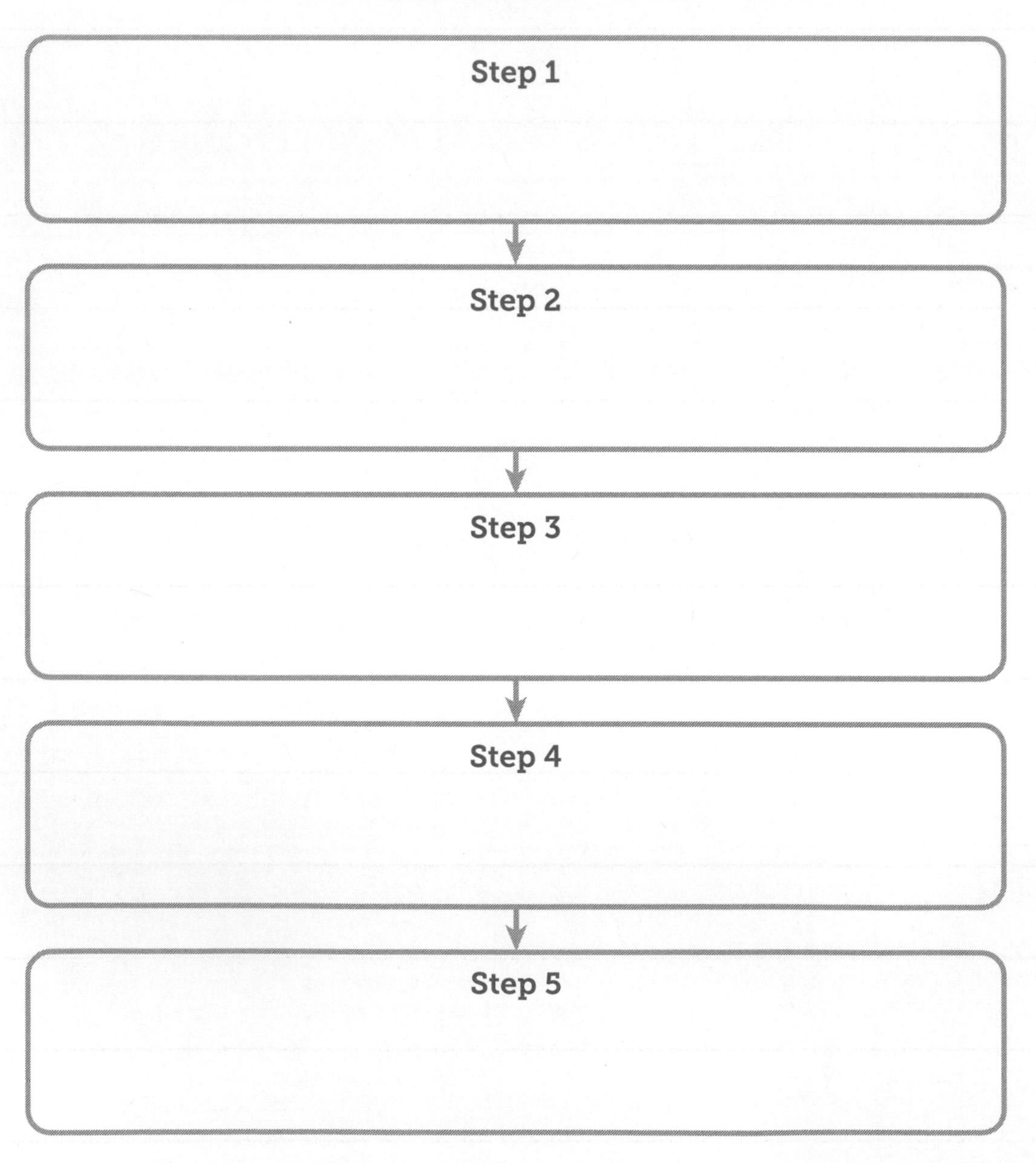

Directions: Read the passage. Then answer the questions that follow it.

Treasures in a Pinecone

By Jan Black

1 One warm day when I was walking in my backyard, I saw a pinecone on the ground. I picked it up, and some seeds fell out of it. Those seeds would be a tasty treat for a squirrel, I thought. Would a squirrel find the seeds in time for dinner?

2 I realized that pinecones were not always open like this one. Sometimes cones were tightly closed. I decided to find out why.

3 I read about pinecones in books and on the Internet. I interviewed a pinecone expert. I gathered pinecones from my backyard and kept them outside on my deck. I watched them for over a year. Here's what I learned.

4 Pinecones open and close slowly as the weather changes. When it's cold or wet, cones are tightly closed. This protects the seeds inside from rain and snow.

5 When the weather becomes warm and dry, pinecones open. In a forest of pine trees on a hot day, you might even hear the crackling sound of cones popping open. The seeds inside may then fall to the ground. The wind may blow the seeds to places where they can grow into new pine trees. A seed has a better chance of taking root and growing when the weather is warm.

Seeds Are Food, Too

6 "Pine seeds are an important source of food for many animals," says Monty Maldonado. He is a pinecone expert with the United States Forest Service. He says squirrels depend on pinecone seeds for most of their meals. They spend lots of time gathering and storing the cones. Maldonado says some animals eat only the seeds from a pinecone. But red squirrels and gray squirrels will eat the whole thing.

7 Small animals aren't the only creatures who eat pine seeds. Maldonado says big grizzly bears and people eat them, too.

8 You may have eaten the seeds of the pinyon pine, which grows in the western United States. These seeds are also known as pinyon nuts, or pine nuts. They are used in salads, puddings, cakes, candy, cookies, and pesto sauce.

9 Seeds inside a pinecone are important for the growth of new trees and as food for animals. It is the pinecone's job to protect and release them. So take note of the pinecones you see on the ground. They hold treasures inside.

See for Yourself!

Find some pinecones and keep them outside where you can look at them for several months. Take a photo or draw a picture of your pinecones when you first get them. Make more pictures as the cones change. In a notebook, keep track of changes in the weather. Write down what happens to your pinecones. Do some of the cones open or close more quickly than others?

You may see signs that a squirrel or another small animal has torn your pinecones apart, looking for seeds to eat.

Directions: Answer the following questions. If you need more space to write an answer, write your answer on your own paper.

131 What is the most important purpose of the first two paragraphs?

A to tell where the author found the pinecones

B to tell why the author became interested in pinecones

C to tell when the author first saw the pinecones

D to tell how the pinecone got in the backyard

132 Read these sentences from the article.

> ***"The seeds inside may then fall to the ground. The wind may blow the seeds to places where they can grow into new pine trees."***

Which of these describes how the two sentences are organized?

A by describing events in the order they occur

B by stating a problem and then its solution

C by giving a cause and then its effect

D by comparing two events

133 One way the author found out about pinecones was by watching them for over a year. Complete the web by listing **three** more ways the author learned about pinecones.

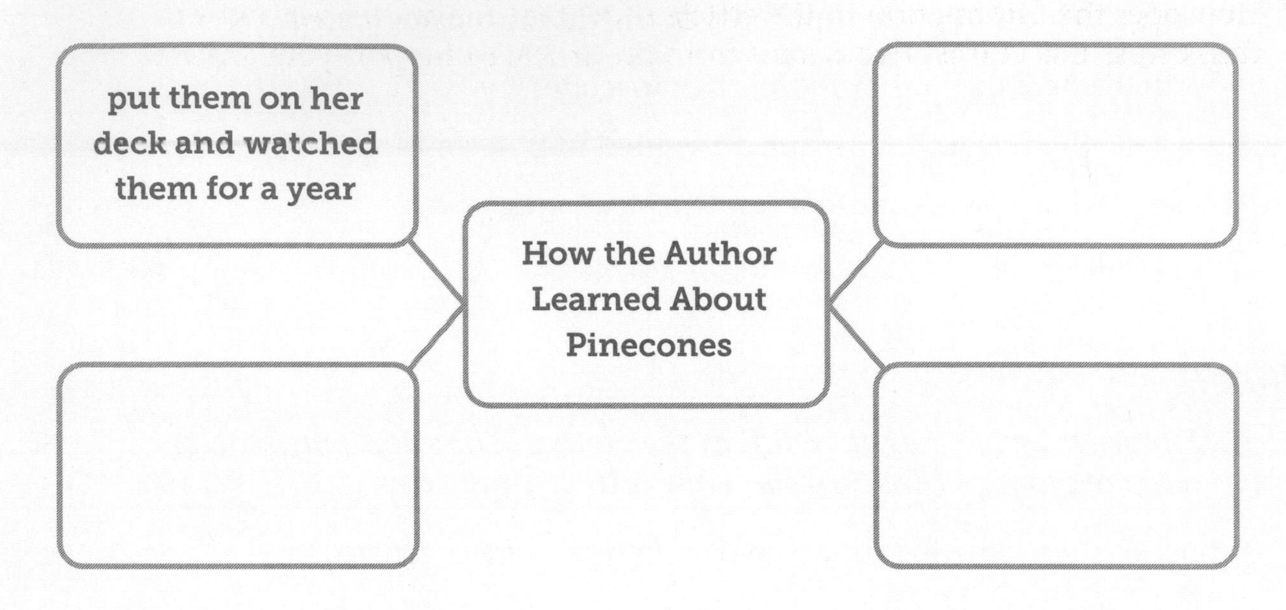

134 The article explains that pinecones open when it is warm and dry. What happens when pinecones open? What is the benefit of opening in warm weather instead of cold weather? Use details from the article to support your answer.

135 Read this sentence from the first paragraph.

"Those seeds would be a tasty treat for a squirrel, I thought."

How does the information in the article show that the author was right to think this? Use at least **two** details from the article to support your answer.

136 The author includes quotes from pinecone expert Monty Maldonado. What main idea do the quotes best support? Use at least **two** details from the article to support your answer.

137 Look closely at the photographs of the pinecones on page 148. How do the photographs help readers understand how pinecones change? Use details from the article to support your answer.

138 What is the main purpose of the section titled "See for Yourself!"? How is this section related to the rest of the article? Use details from the article to support your answer.

139 The author ends the article by saying that pinecones "hold treasures inside." Describe what is found inside pinecones. Include **three** examples of the purpose of these "treasures" in your answer. Use details from the article to support your answer.

Planning Space

You can complete the graphic organizer below to help plan your answer.

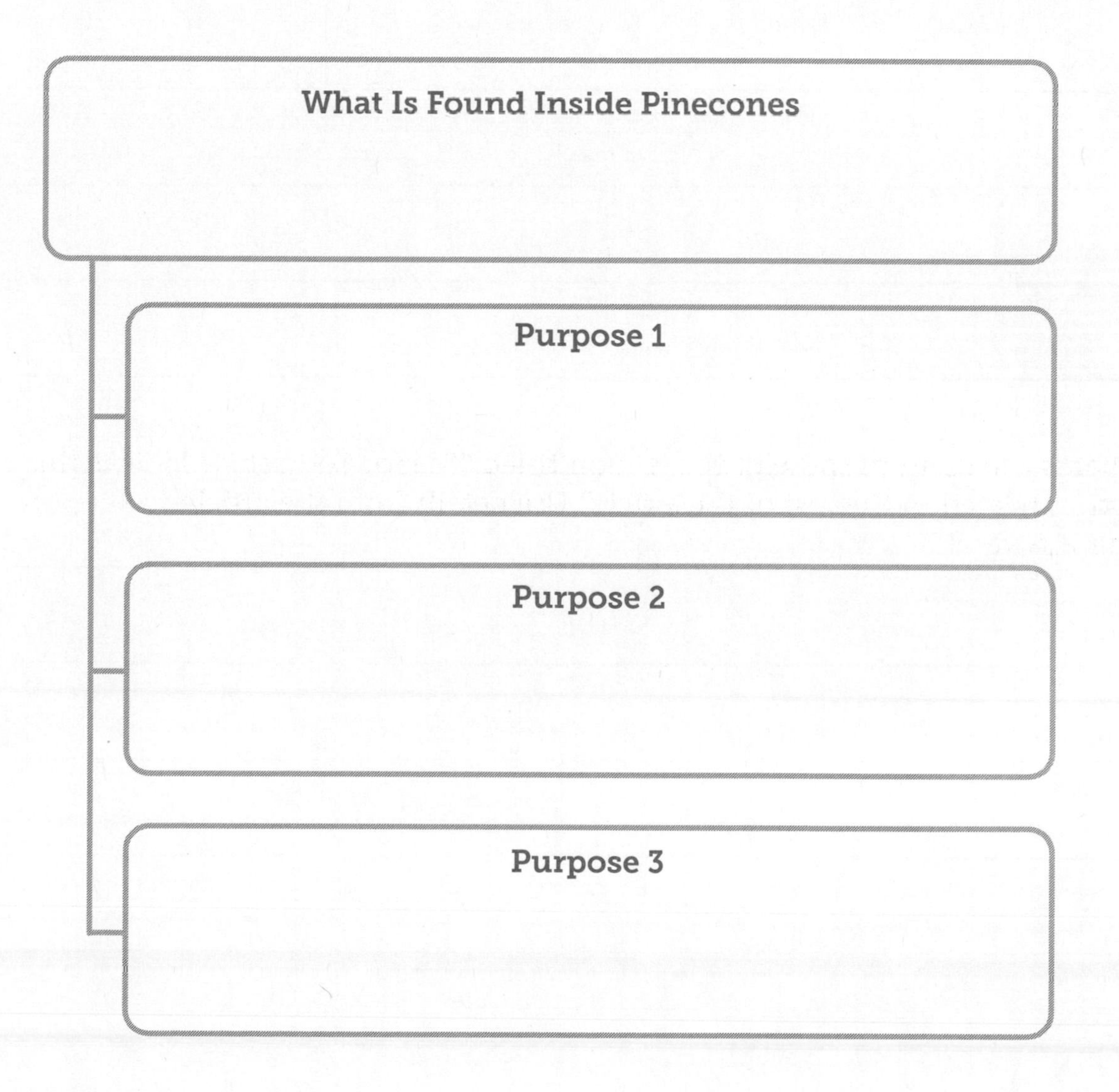

140 Read these sentences from "See for Yourself!"

> ***"Take a photo or draw a picture of your pinecones when you first get them. Make more pictures as the cones change. In a notebook, keep track of changes in the weather."***

What would you expect to find if you kept this information? What link would you expect to see between the weather and what the pinecones look like? Use details from the article to support your answer.

Planning Space

You can write notes, make a list, or draw a chart to help plan your answer.

Directions: Read the following two passages. Then answer the questions that follow.

On the Trail with the Dogies

By John I. White

1 As the sun's first rays appear in the sky, the sleepy cook stirs a pot of food on the campfire. Then he picks up a pan and beats on it with a large spoon. "Come and get it before I throw it in the creek!" he shouts.

2 The cowboys jump out of their bedrolls. The camp is suddenly alive. The men are ready for a big breakfast and another day on the cow trail.

3 After eating, the men put saddles on their horses. They begin getting the cattle onto the trail. They must give extra care to the *dogies* (DOE-gees), calves that don't have a mother. For days, the men have been traveling with their cattle from a ranch to a railroad town. There the cattle will be sold and put on a train to the market.

4 A little over one hundred years ago, this scene was common in the American West. Not many people lived in the region. There were few railroads. The only way to get cattle to the railroad was to walk them there. So that the cattle wouldn't lose any fat, the men would let them graze for an hour every morning and afternoon.

5 It was a colorful, noisy scene. The cattle were bawling. The sun was shining. Now and then a cowboy called after a pesky dogie. A herd of 2,000 stretched for nearly a mile. Two men, called point men, rode up front, guiding the lead cattle. Cowboys rode along the sides and in the back. They pulled their bandannas over their mouths and noses to keep out the dust.

6 Somewhere off to the side rode the horse wrangler. He was usually a teenager and the youngest member of the crew. He took care of the four or five extra ponies each cowboy needed. To give the hard-working horses a rest, cowboys rode on different horses along the way. The trail boss rode on ahead to pick out the route. He also decided where to stop to eat lunch and where to set up camp at night. Following close behind him was the chuck wagon, pulled by two horses and driven by the cook. The wagon carried food and cooking tools, as well as each cowboy's bedroll and personal things.

7 The dogies and adult cattle were handed over at the railroad. Each cowboy would take his pay and relax in town for a few days. Most of the men needed haircuts, new shirts, and pants.

8 On the way home, some cowboys grumbled about their difficult job. But it was a job that most of them loved. And they would soon be on the trail with another herd, doing it all again.

Chuck wagons like this one carried food and supplies—not cowboys!

Cowboy from Head to Toe

By Kathleen Nyquist

1 Many people today wear western clothes because they like the style. Cowboys and cowgirls choose clothes for their usefulness.

2 In the late 1800s, many cowboys lived outdoors. They carried all of their supplies on a horse. They needed useful, durable clothes for life in the wilderness.

3 A cowboy used his hat, or "Stetson," for many things. (John B. Stetson invented the felt cowboy hat.) A cowboy's hat kept rain from his neck and sun from his face. Oats for horses could be put inside. Hats could hold water for drinking or putting out fires. A cowboy could wave his hat as a signal.

4 People could tell by a cowboy's hat where he came from. Men from rainy areas wore hats with a deep crease in the crown. The crease let water drain off easily. In windy areas cowboys wore hats with a low crown. They were less likely to get blown off by the wind. Cowboys from sunny places needed hats with wide brims for shade.

5 Bandannas came in handy, too. Since most shirts were collarless, cowboys used bandannas to help protect their necks from sunburn. They often wore bandannas over their mouths to avoid eating dust kicked up by cattle. If someone broke an arm, the bandanna became a sling until a doctor came. Bandannas were also used as ties when cowboys wanted to dress up.

6 Cowboys often wore wool shirts. Wool absorbed a cowboy's sweat on a hot day. It kept him warm on a cold night. Some cowboys wore shirts made from the skins of deer. Like the fancy western clothes of today, buckskin shirts often had fringe on them.

7 Fringe was first used by Native Americans. Cowboys learned that rainwater slipped off the thin strips. This kept clothes from getting soaked. Cowboys could also cut off the long leather fringe to fix fences or whatever needed tying.

8 Cowboys often wore vests over their shirts. Vests kept out cold winds, and cowboys could move easily in them. Also, vests had pockets. (Most shirts didn't.) Cowboys needed vest pockets to carry matches, gold nuggets, and notebooks for recording cattle brands.

9 Shirts were tucked into heavy-duty pants, such as Levi's jeans. (These were invented by Levi Strauss in the mid-1800s.) A cowboy could ride many rough trails before his jeans wore out.

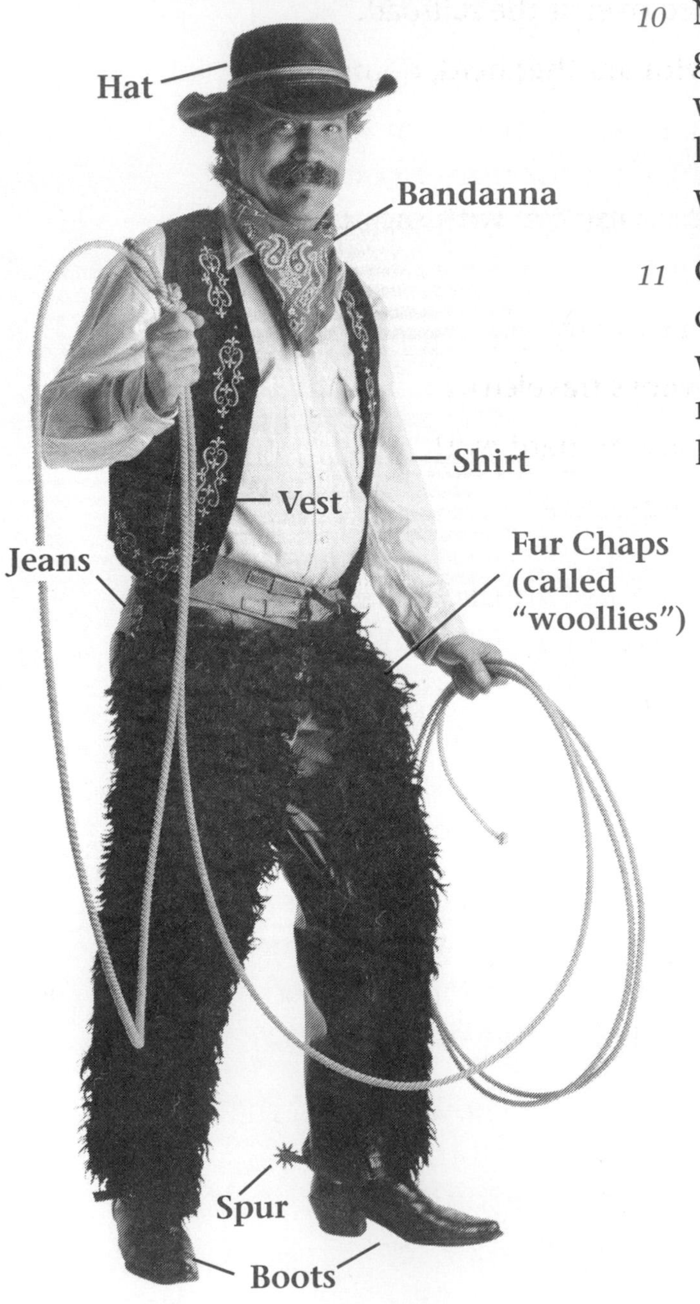

10 Mexican cowboys, called *vaqueros*, gave American cowboys the idea of wearing *chaps*. These large pieces of leather protected legs from thorns, wire fences, and kicking cattle.

11 Of course, a cowboy wouldn't be complete without boots. These were useful, too. The pointed toes made it easy for a cowboy to slip his feet into stirrups. The raised heels kept his feet from slipping out. When roping cattle on foot, a cowboy dug his big bootheels into the dirt to keep from falling. Spiked wheels, called *spurs*, were usually filed until blunt, then attached to bootheels. They were used to give signals to the horse.

12 Cowboys and cowgirls today wear many of the same types of clothes as cowboys of the late 1800s. Fashions change, but useful work clothes never go out of style.

Directions: Use "On the Trail with the Dogies" to answer the following questions. If you need more space to write an answer, write your answer on your own paper.

141 Which sentence from the article would be the best caption for the photograph at the beginning?

- **A** "The men are ready for a big breakfast and another day on the cow trail."
- **B** "A herd of 2,000 stretched for nearly a mile."
- **C** "The dogies and adult cattle were handed over at the railroad."
- **D** "And they would soon be on the trail with another herd, doing it all again."

142 What is the main reason the author includes a caption with the photograph of the wagon?

- **A** to show that cowboys could not take many items
- **B** to help readers understand how the cowboys traveled
- **C** to suggest that being a cowboy was not always hard work
- **D** to explain why the chuck wagons were important

143 The article describes how different people on the trail have different jobs to do. Complete the chart below by adding the tasks of the people listed.

People	Tasks
Point Men	
Horse Wrangler	
Trail Boss	

144 In the second paragraph, the author states that the "camp is suddenly alive." Explain what this tells you about what the camp is like. Give **two** reasons the camp is like this. Use details from the article to support your answer.

Directions: Use "Cowboy from Head to Toe" to answer the following questions. If you need more space to write an answer, write your answer on your own paper.

145 Which item of clothing shown in the diagram could have been shown placed somewhere else? Explain why you chose that item and where else it could have been placed. Use details from the article to support your answer.

146 The article describes how a cowboy's hat had many purposes. Complete the web below by describing **three** more uses of a cowboy's hat.

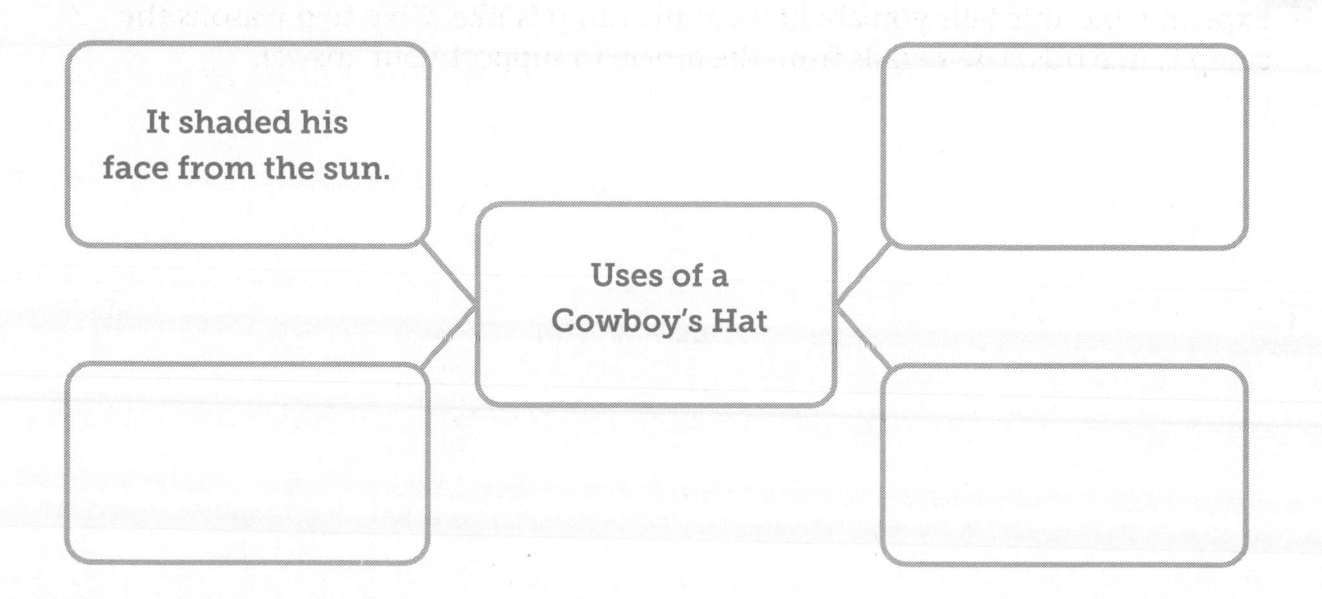

147 The title and the diagram both show the main ideas of the article. Describe how the title and the diagram are related. How do they both summarize the main ideas of the article? Use details from the article to support your answer.

148 The article describes how a cowboy's clothes gave protection against the weather. How does the article show that the clothes were useful in all types of weather? Give at least **three** specific examples from the article to support your answer.

Directions: Use both "On the Trail with the Dogies" and "Cowboy from Head to Toe" to answer the following questions.

149 "Cowboy from Head to Toe" describes how each item had many different uses. How does the information in "On the Trail with the Dogies" show why it would be good for one item to have many uses? Use details from both articles to support your answer.

Planning Space

You can write notes, make a list, or draw a chart to help plan your answer.

150 Both articles are about the lives of cowboys. How is the focus of each article different? Which article best shows that life was hard for the cowboys? Use details from both articles to support your answer.

Planning Space

You can write notes, make a list, or draw a chart to help plan your answer.

Directions: Read the passage. Then answer the questions that follow it.

Clever Hodja, Foolish Hodja

A Turkish Tale Retold by Gale Sypher Jacob

1 *Nasreddin Hodja was probably a real person who lived in Turkey in the thirteenth century. He is famous in folklore for being both clever and foolish.*

Clever Hodja

2 Late one hot summer afternoon, Nasreddin Hodja strode through his town of Ak Sehir (AHK sheh-heer), heading toward the palace of Tamerlane the Great. Hodja carried an offering—a fat goose roasted to a gleaming brown by his wife, Fatima. Drops of sweat dripped under Hodja's turban and loose, flowing kaftan. His stomach felt tight with hunger.

3 Outside town, Hodja stopped to rest under a walnut tree. He pinched his nose, trying to close out the tempting smell of freshly roasted goose. Then, before he could stop himself, he ripped a crispy brown leg from the goose and gobbled down the tender meat. Delicious!

4 He threw the bone into the dusty roadside weeds, licked his fingers, picked up the goose, and walked on.

5 As he entered the palace, Hodja wondered how he could explain the one-legged goose. Ever since Tamerlane had conquered Ak Sehir, he and Hodja had enjoyed each other's company. Still, Hodja feared offending the powerful ruler.

6 "A tasty goose roasted this very morning by my wife, Fatima," said Hodja, bowing and presenting the platter to Tamerlane.

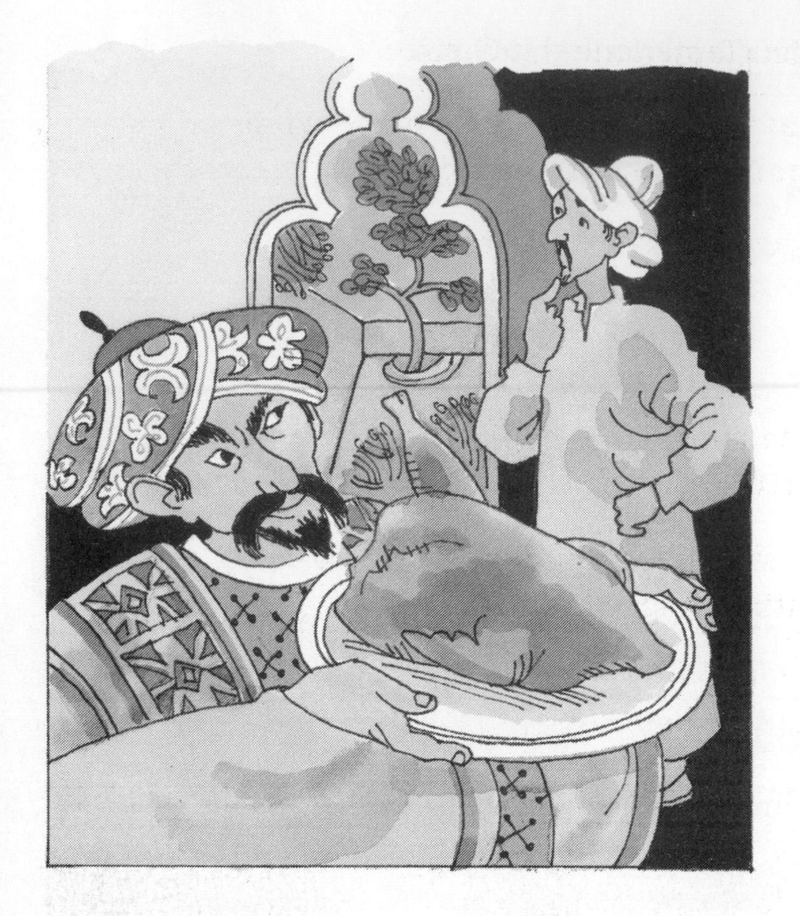

7 "I've heard that your wife is an excellent cook," replied Tamerlane. "But what is this? The goose has only one leg! Where I come from, geese have two legs."

8 Hodja stood there, looking out the window. His brain buzzed like bees around flowers, searching for an explanation.

9 "The geese of Ak Sehir are famous for having only one leg," declared Nasreddin Hodja. "Just look out into the palace garden."

10 "Oh, Hodja, don't be foolish," said Tamerlane with a chuckle.

11 "Let's go and see," insisted Hodja. They walked outside.

12 In the sun-baked garden, near the fountain, stood a flock of sleeping white geese, each balanced on one yellow leg.

13 "Perhaps I've been too busy to notice," said Tamerlane, "but you are correct. I see only one leg for each goose."

14 Hodja, who was anxious to be gone before the geese woke up, said, "Enjoy the goose. Peace be with you." Then he turned to leave.

15 Just as Nasreddin Hodja reached the garden gate, Tamerlane called for a servant by clapping his hands twice. The two loud claps woke the flock of geese. Flapping and hissing, the geese ran off—each on two yellow legs.

16 "Ah, Hodja, you fooled me," cried Tamerlane the Great.

17 Hodja called back, "I should have clapped my hands twice before Fatima cooked the goose—then it would have had two legs."

18 Tamerlane laughed as Hodja waved and disappeared.

Foolish Hodja

19 That evening, Hodja told Fatima about their goose. "I fooled Tamerlane the Great!" he boasted.

20 "You spoiled my perfect goose!" she cried. "But you were also very clever ... instead of foolish." Fatima hugged him.

21 Hodja smiled. "Me? Foolish?" "Only once in a while," Fatima replied, and they kissed each other good-night.

22 Sometime after midnight, Hodja woke and was thirsty. The water jug near the bed was empty, so he drowsily plodded outside to draw water from the well. The wind whispered in the cypress trees.

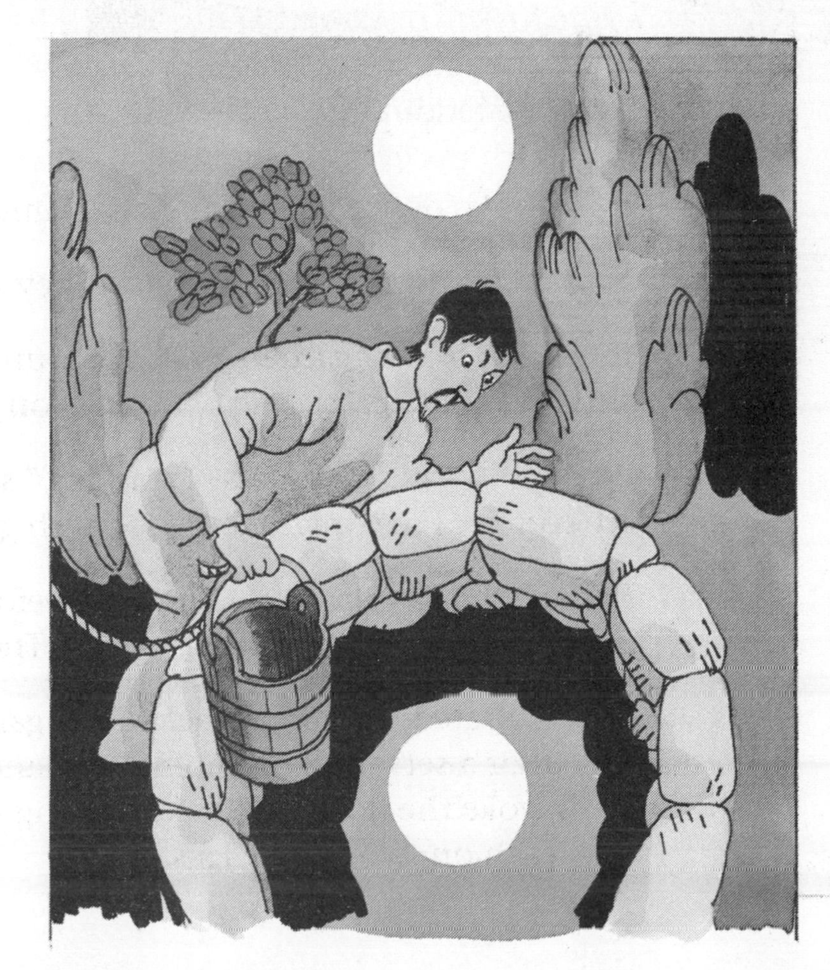

23 Half awake, Hodja leaned over the well to lower the bucket. Then his sleepy eyes popped open.

24 "The moon has fallen into the well!" he cried, his thirst forgotten. "It's sitting down there, all shiny and round!"

25 He lowered the bucket into the well and shouted, "Moon, you won't drown—I'll rescue you!"

26 Hodja felt the bucket scraping the jagged rocks inside the well as he let it down. *Splash!* He heard the bucket hit the water. "Hop in the bucket, Moon," Hodja called. "I'll pull you up."

27 Hodja braced himself against the side of the well and pulled. The bucket did not move.

28 *Good! The moon has climbed into the bucket,* thought Hodja. "Hold on tight!" he cried.

29 Hodja pulled harder. Nothing happened.

30 "Moon, I'll save you if it takes all my strength!" Hodja called.

31 He drew a long breath, tightened every muscle, and yanked. *CRACK!* The bucket's handle, which had been caught under a rock, jumped loose, and the bucket flew out of the well. *SMACK!* It hit Nasreddin Hodja, knocking him over. He lay there on his back with his eyes closed, rubbing his head.

32 When Hodja opened his eyes, he looked up into the night sky. "There it is!" he cried. "I've saved the moon!"

Directions: Answer the following questions. If you need more space to write an answer, write your answer on your own paper.

151 Based on Hodja's actions in both sections, which word best describes him?

A selfish

B funny

C polite

D sly

152 Which event from the story is NOT meant to add humor?

A Hodja eating one of the legs of the goose.

B The geese racing off on two legs when Tamerlane claps.

C Hodja seeing the moon in the bottom of the well.

D The bucket flying out of the well and hitting Hodja.

153 At the start of the story, Hodja knows that he should not eat the goose but he does anyway. Explain why Hodja eats the goose. Use at least **two** details from the story to support your answer.

154 Read this sentence from the story.

"His brain buzzed like bees around flowers, searching for an explanation."

Explain how the illustration helps show what this sentence tells about how Hodja feels. Use details from the story to support your answer.

155 The illustration in the section "Clever Hodja" represents the main problem in the section. Complete the chart below by listing **two** more details shown in the illustration and explaining what each detail shows about the main problem.

Detail	Main Problem
Hodja looks puzzled.	**Hodja does not know how to explain the missing leg.**

156 Hodja fools Tamerlane into thinking that all the geese only have one leg. Is Tamerlane mad when he realizes he has been tricked? Use at least **two** details from the story to support your conclusion.

157 Read the first three paragraphs of the section "Foolish Hodja." What do Fatima's words suggest about what the section will be about? Use details from the story to support your answer.

158 Look closely at the illustration in the section "Foolish Hodja." How does the illustration show that the moon has not really fallen into the well? Use details from the story to support your answer.

159 What does Hodja think is happening when he is trying to save the moon? How is what the reader knows different from what Hodja knows? Explain how this affects the story. Use details from the story to support your answer.

Planning Space

You can complete the chart below to help plan your answer.

	What Hodja Thinks	What the Reader Knows
When Hodja sees the moon in the well		
When Hodja cannot pull the moon up		
When Hodja sees the moon in the sky		

160 The two stories about Hodja show that he is sometimes clever and sometimes foolish. Identify **three** features of the story the author uses to show that Hodja has two sides. Explain how each feature shows that Hodja has two sides.

Planning Space

You can write notes, make a list, or draw a chart to help plan your answer.

Directions: Read the following two passages. Then answer the questions that follow.

Dogs at Work

By Sherry Shahan

1 In an ancient house, a mosaic was found that said *cave canem*. In Latin, that means "Beware of the dog." Being a watchdog is one of many jobs that our four-legged friends have done over the years.

2 Dogs not only protect property, but they also herd sheep, pull sleds, and rescue people. They are experts at sniffing out everything from fruits and vegetables to human beings. And at the end of a hard day's work, dogs still like to play!

3 There are many kinds of **search-and-rescue dogs**. They are trained to help people in trouble. The canine workers that help the ski patrol are called **avalanche dogs**. An avalanche occurs when a large mass of snow slides down a mountain. Every year, many people are trapped beneath snow from avalanches.

4 Skilak has been trained to smell the human scent through ice crystals. As soon as he locates a person, he barks. Then Pat, the ski patrolman, gives the order "Search!" Skilak quickly digs out the person.

5 The main task of **sheepherding dogs** is to control a flock of sheep. The dogs bark to move a flock from field to field. Sometimes they nip at the sheep's feet to urge them on. When it's time to shear the sheep, the dogs nudge them into a pen.

6 The sheepherder commands the dogs by whistling. One whistle means "Round them up!"

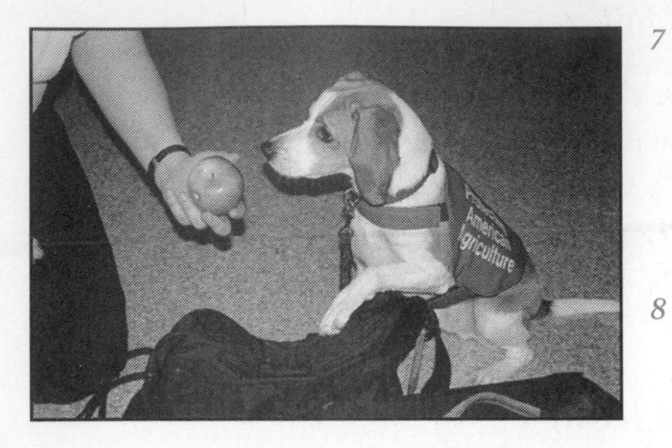

7 **Agriculture dogs** work at airports. They help to prevent harmful insects from coming into the country. These insects may hide in vegetables, fruits, and meats.

8 Hal sniffs suitcases before the owners pick them up. If Hal smells food hidden inside, he sits down next to the suitcase. This signal tells the inspector to check that suitcase.

9 Long before airplanes were invented, **sled dogs** transported goods in snowy regions. Back then, dog teams pulled heavy loads of food and supplies. They even helped to deliver mail to remote villages. Today, sled dogs still help people to get around. They also compete in sled-dog races.

10 **Service dogs** help people to do things that the people can't do themselves.

11 Tijo (shown here) is handing a library book to Michelle, his owner. He can also open doors using a special hook. Tijo even helps to make Michelle's bed in the morning. How? He picks up stuffed animals and tosses them in place. Above all, Tijo is a loving friend.

Doctor Dog

By Jennifer Mattox

1 The sun is not up yet, but a three-year-old dog named Ansley is on his way to work. He works at Nationwide Children's Hospital helping children who need therapy. The therapy helps kids learn skills again after they've been sick or injured.

2 Ansley's owner is Jenny Lundine. She is a speech therapist. Jenny brings Ansley to see six kids twice every day.

3 Ansley plays fetch with kids who need to make their arms or legs stronger. Kids who have lost speech skills learn how to talk again. They give Ansley commands such as "sit," "stand," and "roll over." Kids who have trouble remembering can learn by giving Ansley commands in a certain order.

A Friendly Furry Face

4 Part of Ansley's job is to make kids feel happier. One patient, a two-year-old girl, often wakes up cranky because of her illness. When Jenny says, "Up," Ansley puts his front paws on the little girl's bed. The girl rolls over to see Ansley's friendly furry face. She smiles. During group therapy, the kids do a cheer to encourage one another. Ansley wears big sunglasses and holds a pompom in his mouth. "Ansley adds an exciting layer to what we are already doing," says Jenny.

5 When someone gives Ansley the command "lap," he gently places his paws on the child's lap. Most children love it when Ansley is told to "jump" on their beds so they can pet him. He can also walk backward, turn off lights, and shut doors. He knows forty commands in all. He learned them when he spent six months at a special dog school called Canine Companions for Independence.

Healing Fun

6 Ansley can't give medicine or take X-rays, but he can help kids get better. When the kids don't feel like doing their therapy, Ansley makes it more fun. Having fun helps the kids work harder and heal faster.

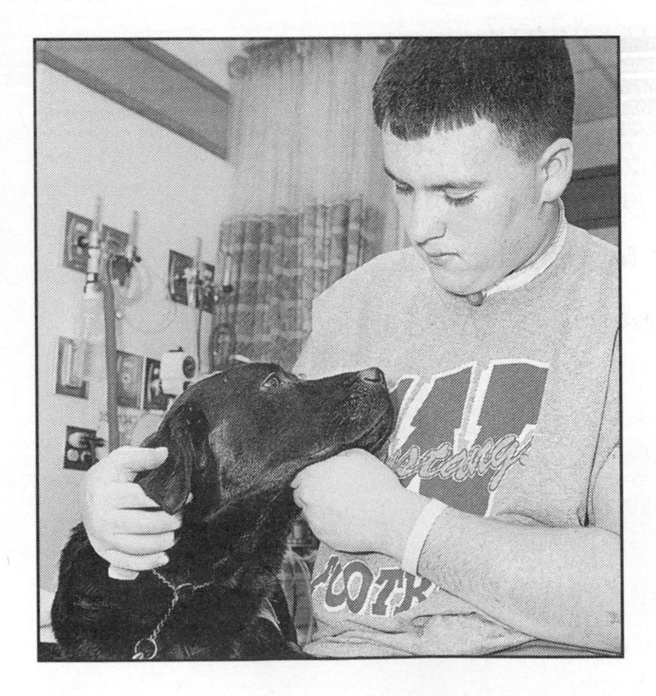

7 After a long day at the hospital, Ansley and Jenny are ready to return home. Tomorrow, Doctor Dog will rise early and do it all again. Ansley's job may sound like a lot for a dog. But smart, energetic dogs like Ansley seem to enjoy working. And for the kids at Nationwide Children's Hospital, he's the perfect medicine.

Directions: Use "Dogs at Work" to answer the following questions. If you need more space to write an answer, write your answer on your own paper.

161 Which type of dog is shown in the photograph on page 183?

A search-and-rescue dog

B sheepherding dog

C agriculture dog

D service dog

162 What is the main purpose of the first paragraph of the article?

A to explain why dogs are important to people

B to describe how dogs were not kept as pets in the past

C to show that being a watchdog is the most common job of dogs

D to introduce the topic with an interesting fact

163 How is the information in paragraph 9 mainly organized?

A It compares how sled dogs are used now to how they were used in the past.

B It describes the main reasons that sled dogs are not often used today.

C It gives an example of how life has changed for one sled dog.

D It states an opinion on sled dogs and then supports it with facts.

164 How is the work of an avalanche dog similar to the work of an agriculture dog? Describe the main skill that is used by both types of dogs. Use details from the article to support your answer.

Directions: Use "Doctor Dog" to answer the following questions. If you need more space to write an answer, write your answer on your own paper.

165 How does the first paragraph of the article make it seem like Ansley is a person? What is the most likely reason the author does this? Use details from the article to support your answer.

166 The article describes how Ansley helps children in different ways. Give **two** examples of how speaking to Ansley helps kids. Use details from the article to support your answer.

167 Look at the illustration in the article. Is the illustration funny or serious? Do you think the illustration helps the article make its point? Use details from the article to support your answer.

168 Read the first sentence of the section titled "A Friendly Furry Face."

"Part of Ansley's job is to make kids feel happier."

How does the rest of the information in the section support this statement? Use at least **two** details from the section to support your answer.

Directions: Use both "Dogs at Work" and "Doctor Dog" to answer the following questions. If you need more space to write an answer, write your answer on your own paper.

169 The information about service dogs in "Dogs at Work" describes a dog named Tijo. How is the work of Tijo similar to the work of Ansley? Use details from both articles to support your answer.

170 Both "Dogs at Work" and "Doctor Dog" describe the uses of dogs. Write an essay in which you explain why dogs are useful. Describe at least **three** important uses of dogs in your essay. Use information from both articles to support your answer.

Planning Space

You can complete the chart below to help plan your answer.

Use of Dogs	Supporting Details

Directions: Read the passage. Then answer the questions that follow it.

The Year the Pilgrims Stepped on Governor Bradford

By David L. Roper

1 I was backstage, sweating in a Pilgrim costume. It was the night of the annual Thanksgiving play, and I was nervous.

2 The play had been written by Mr. Meriwether and had been performed by fourth- and fifth-grade students every year forever. But last year some kids forgot their parts, so Mr. M. announced that we would do the play differently this time. "We will have a narrator," he said. He picked a fourth-grader named Bob. Bob was little, but he had a BIG VOICE. We called him "Boomer."

3 Mr. M. gave Boomer a stack of cards. I caught a glimpse of the one on top. It had a few words written in big block letters. Mr. M. had told Boomer, "All you have to do is read the cards." He'd told us, "All you have to do is act out what Bob reads. It's foolproof." We'd practiced some, but I was still nervous.

4 The night of the play, the auditorium was filled with family and friends.

5 I glanced at Boomer. He looked nervous, too. He kept shifting the cards from hand to hand as he wiped his sweaty palms on his pant legs.

6 When the time came for the play to begin, Boomer stepped out in front of the curtains. I could hear him reading from the first card: **"Welcome to the annual performance of *The First Thanksgiving*."**

7 As the curtains opened, Boomer read the second card: **"In 1620, the Pilgrims left England to travel to the New World."** He shifted to the next card: **"They sailed in a small ship called the *Mayflower*."** Several of us Pilgrims grabbed the top edges of a cardboard boat and shuffled onto the stage. **"Much of the journey was through rough seas."** We rocked the boat. **"But at last the ship landed ..."**

8 Boomer wiped one hand on his trousers and started to shift the cards to his other hand. That's when disaster struck. The cards slipped out of Boomer's hands and flew in every direction.

9 Boomer scrambled around, scooping up cards and stacking them in any old order.

10 He started reading again. But the first words on the next card were **"on long wooden tables."** Land the ship on a table? We had been told to act out what Boomer had read.

The rest of the Pilgrims hustled onstage with a picnic table, and we rammed the ship into it. A few people in the audience laughed. **"The tables were loaded down with ..."**

11 Next card: **"... smelly fish ..."** Kids dressed in fish costumes hurried out and climbed onto the table. **"... which were placed in hills of dirt."** A kid rushed onstage and dumped dirt on the table.

12 **"Ninety Native Americans ..."** More kids dashed onstage.

13 **"... brought deer to the feast."** Kids in deer costumes followed. **"The feast lasted ..."**

14 **"... sixty-six days. The Pilgrims stepped out on ..."**

15 **"... Governor William Bradford ..."** The boy playing the governor of the colony shrugged, then lay down on the stage. We Pilgrims put our feet on him. **"... who called for a feast of Thanksgiving."** He waved his arms like he was making a proclamation.

16 By this time, the audience was howling. Boomer kept reading.

17 **"They had wild ducks, geese, turkeys, mashed pumpkin, and lots of vegetables."** Kids in bird and vegetable costumes crowded the stage, bumping into one another. **"The people ate and ate ..."**

18 The following card began: **"... which was exhausting work."** We all grabbed our stomachs and plopped down.

19 Boomer came to the card that was supposed to be the last in the stack: **"What are we thankful for?"** He threw the rest of the cards in the air and said, **"I'm thankful that this is over!"** He sprawled out on the stage.

20 We got a standing ovation.

21 That was the only year that the cards were used. The next year, we practiced and practiced our parts, and the play went OK. But people still talk about the year that the Pilgrims stepped on Governor Bradford.

Directions: Answer the following questions. If you need more space to write an answer, write your answer on your own paper.

171 The first paragraph is mainly included to introduce the

A setting

B main character

C main problem

D theme

172 What does the art at the start of the story mainly show about Boomer?

A how loud his voice is

B how short he is

C how excited he was

D how nervous he felt

173 Read this sentence from paragraph 5.

"He kept shifting the cards from hand to hand as he wiped his sweaty palms on his pant legs."

Which statement best explains why this detail is important?

A It tells how Boomer wanted a part in the play.

B It helps show why Boomer dropped the cards.

C It shows that Boomer was too young to be the narrator.

D It suggests that Boomer dropped the cards on purpose.

174 Read the sentences from paragraph 3.

> ***Mr. M. had told Boomer, "All you have to do is read the cards." He'd told us, "All you have to do is act out what Bob reads. It's foolproof."***

Describe **two** important details given in these sentences. Tell how the two details help explain why things go wrong. Use details from the story to support your answer.

175 The author includes words in bold throughout the story. Explain what the words in bold represent. Why are the words in bold important to the plot of the story? Use details from the story to support your answer.

176 Look closely at the illustration of Boomer dropping the cards. Does the illustration make the event seem serious or funny? Use at least **two** specific details from the illustration to support your conclusion.

177 How did Mr. Meriwether most likely feel at the end of the story? Explain how you think he would have felt about his decision to use a narrator. Use at least **two** details from the story to support your answer.

178 In paragraph 2, the author explains that Bob was chosen as narrator because of his big voice. Give **two** examples of ways the author emphasizes how big Bob's voice was.

179 Read this sentence from the end of the story.

> ***"But people still talk about the year that the Pilgrims stepped on Governor Bradford."***

Explain why people probably still talk about the events. Use details from the story to support your answer.

180 The illustration on page 196 shows events that happened during the play. How does the illustration help show the humor of the events? Give at least **three** examples of humorous events from the illustration in your answer.

Planning Space

You can complete the chart below to help plan your answer.

Detail from Art	How the Detail Adds Humor

Part D:

All Together

Literary, Informational, and Paired Passages with Multiple Choice, Short Response, Extended Response, and Essay Questions

Common Core State Standards for Informational Text (Grade 3)

The questions in Part D cover the standards in all three sections of the standards.

Key Ideas and Details: RI.3.1, RI.3.2, RI.3.3

Craft and Structure: RI.3.4, RI.3.5, RI.3.6

Integration of Knowledge and Ideas: RI.3.7, RI.3.8, RI.3.9

Common Core State Standards for Literary Text (Grade 3)

The questions in Part D cover the standards in all three sections of the standards.

Key Ideas and Details: RL.3.1, RL.3.2, RL.3.3

Craft and Structure: RL.3.4, RL.3.5, RL.3.6

Integration of Knowledge and Ideas: RL.3.7, RL.3.9

Directions: Read the passage. Then answer the questions that follow it.

Make Way! It's the Children's Parade!

By Dan Risch

1 It's early morning. Work crews hang Norwegian flags from lampposts along the main street in Decorah, Iowa. As the sun rises, the breeze freshens and the flags start to ripple. Courthouse Square begins to fill with kids let out of school.

2 It's May 17, and the kids have something special to do!

3 Red, blue, and white Norwegian flags are handed out. Some of the kids practice dance steps from the Trip to Helsinki or the Mountain March. All the kids shuffle into position. First, the Nordic Dancers. Next, the fourth- and fifth-graders of St. Benedict's, then West Side Elementary. A long banner is unfurled at the front. Two students raise flags: one American, one Norwegian.

4 Everything's in place.

5 A signal is given and the kids roar: "Hooray! Hooray! Hooray!"

6 The Children's Parade is on its way.

7 The tradition of Norway's Children's Parade began in 1814, when Norway was governed by Sweden. Norwegians wanted to rule themselves like the people in the United States. So on May 17,

1814, Norway followed the United States' example and wrote its own constitution.

8 At that time, though, Sweden wasn't ready to let Norway go. Norwegians continued to hope for the day that they would govern themselves. To remind Sweden—peacefully—that they wanted independence, every May 17, Norwegians marched in parades led by children. The Children's Parade of Syttende Mai (Norwegian for May 17) was born.

9 Finally, in 1905, Norway got its wish and became independent.

10 Today, wherever people of Norwegian heritage live, spring blossoms with celebrations on May 17. In fact, the path of Norwegian immigrants settling across America in the 1800s can be traced by where Syttende Mai celebrations take place. Parades are held in New York, where the first Norwegian immigrants gathered, and in Illinois, Iowa, Wisconsin, Minnesota, and Seattle, Washington.

11 In Norway, the morning of May 17 starts much as it does in Decorah and other Norwegian American communities. "Kids gather at the school, and we march to the church," says Ivar Lundby, a student in Oestfold County, Norway. "We all carry flags, and the school band plays."

12 Anna Sofie, another Oestfold County student, explains why children lead the parades. "Children and families are most important. And we march as representatives of our country." She adds, "Kids ... have fun, too. I like waving the flag behind our marching band. And the best thing is wearing my special *bunad* [Norway's national costume]."

13 Fun is also on the march in Decorah. "I like marching because it's fun to walk with your friends on a special day," says fourth-grader Laura Munkle.

14 Classmate Rita Marie Guzman adds, "It's great when the kids can shout without teachers telling them not to." And like Ivar and Anna in Norway, Jacob Stock enjoys waving at people watching the parade. But he also points out that "the parade's important because it's [a reminder of how] Norway won its freedom from Sweden."

15 Annalise Johnson sums up what she appreciates most about Syttende Mai. "The marching! All the noise and people. And the colors! Red, white, and blue. We were like a giant flag rolling down downtown Decorah."

16 So make way! Here come the kids marching to remember Norway's peaceful separation from Sweden—and to have fun!

Iowa

Sitting in the U.S. Midwest, Iowa has long been known for corn farming. Now it's also known for wind farming. Rows of giant windmills make electricity from winds crossing the Great Plains.

Norway

Norway lies northeast of Great Britain. Half of the country is within the frigid Arctic Circle. Can you guess one of Norway's favorite sports? Skiing!

Directions: Answer the following questions. If you need more space to write an answer, write your answer on your own paper.

181 What is the purpose of the information in paragraphs 7 and 8?

A to tell what the parade is like

B to tell how the parades started

C to tell why the parades are still held

D to tell where parades are held today

182 Read these sentences from the article.

"In fact, the path of Norwegian immigrants settling across America in the 1800s can be traced by where Syttende Mai celebrations take place. Parades are held in New York, where the first Norwegian immigrants gathered, and in Illinois, Iowa, Wisconsin, Minnesota, and Seattle, Washington."

Which of these would most clearly show the path described?

A a table

B a photograph

C a graph

D a map

183 The first six paragraphs describe the start of a parade. Is the parade a serious or a joyful event? Explain how you can tell. Use at least **two** details from the paragraphs to support your answer.

184 The article explains that the parade was started as a way to show that Norway wanted its independence from Sweden. Why were children chosen to lead the parade? Use details from the article to support your conclusion.

185 How does the article show that the people of Norway were patient about getting their independence from Sweden? Use at least **two** details from the article to support your answer.

186 The parade is called the Children's Parade of Syttende Mai. Explain what "Syttende Mai" means and why it is important. Use details from the article to support your answer.

187 Paragraphs 11 and 12 include quotes from students in Norway. Paragraphs 13 and 14 include quotes from students in Decorah, Iowa. What is similar about all the quotes? What does this show about the two parades? Use details from the article to support your answer.

188 Read the quotes of Laura, Rita, and Jacob in paragraphs 13 and 14. How is Jacob's quote different from the others? What does this suggest about what the parade means to him? Use details from the article to support your answer.

189 Think about why the Fourth of July is a holiday in America and the traditions of the day. Describe **three** ways the Fourth of July is like the Children's Parade of Syttende Mai. Use details from the article to support your answer.

Planning Space

You can write notes, make a list, or draw a chart to help plan your answer.

190 How does the article show that Norwegian people living in America have not forgotten their history or culture? Use **three** examples from the article to support your answer.

Planning Space

You can complete the graphic organizer below to help plan your answer.

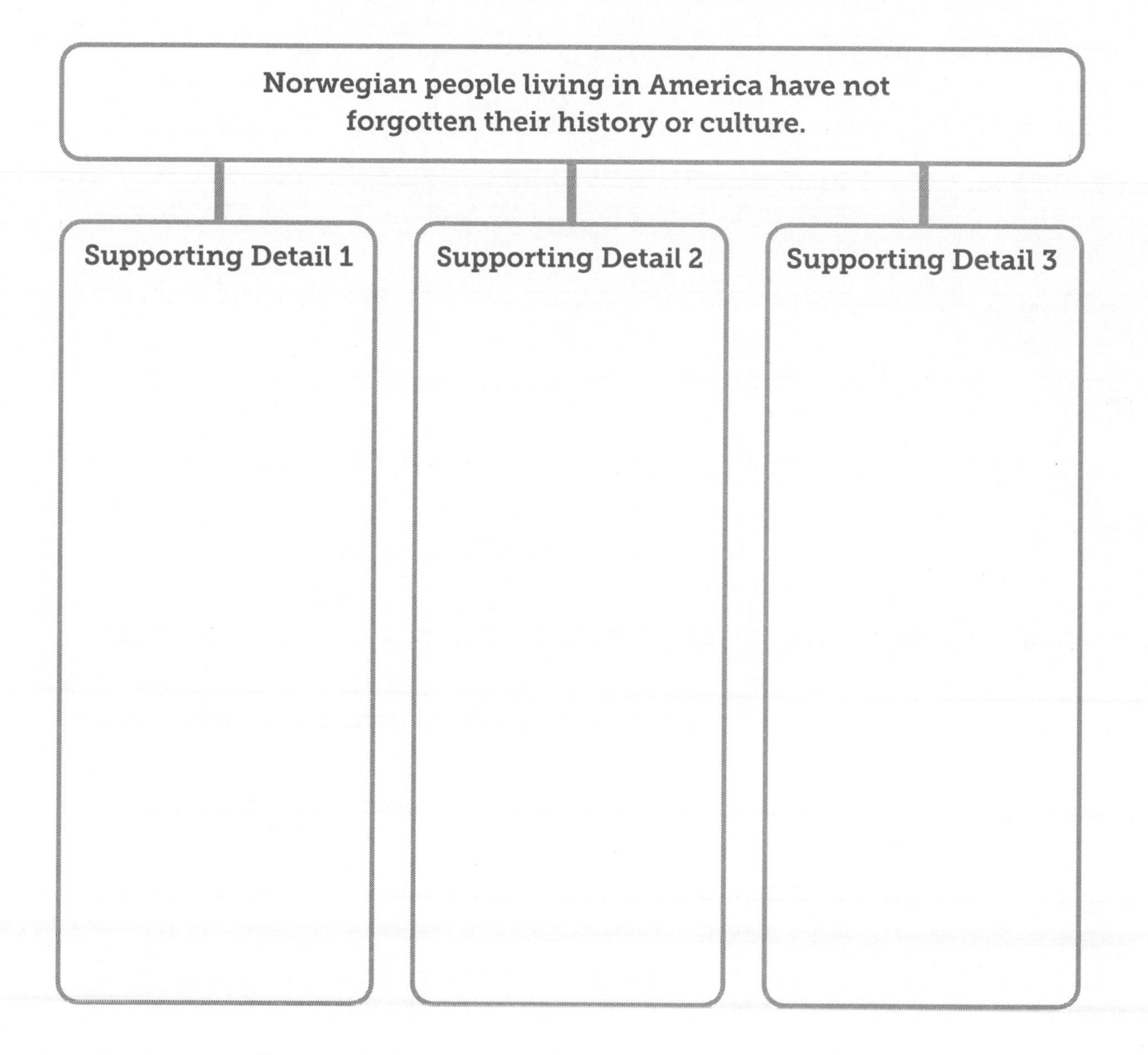

Directions: Read the passage. Then answer the questions that follow it.

Abigail, Enough!

By Wendy Silvano

1 Abigail lived for one thing and one thing only: GYMNASTICS!

2 She did gymnastics all day—anytime, anywhere. She did leaps in the kitchen, front limbers in the den, headstands in the hallway, and back handsprings on her bed.

3 "Abigail, enough!" yelled her brother, Sam, one morning when Abigail was blocking the entryway with her arch. "Do your gymnastics somewhere else!"

4 "Abigail, enough!" moaned her mother one afternoon when she did cartwheels all the way to the car and almost squashed the newly planted daisies. "You can't do gymnastics here."

5 "Abigail, enough!" cried her father one evening when her back walkover almost walked over the cat. "You have to find someplace else to do your gymnastics."

6 Abigail's body begged to bounce. Her legs longed to leap. Her muscles were meant to move. So Abigail had no choice but to look for somewhere new to bend and bounce, twist and twirl, leap and lunge.

7 She tried her bedroom. Too small.

8 She tried the basement. Too low.

9 She tried the backyard. Too many dogs.

10 She tried the garage. Too many tools.

11 "I've got to go to a gym!" declared Abigail.

12 "Too much money!" cried her parents.

13 "Then I'll earn it myself," said Abigail.

14 She set up a lemonade stand. She advertised and publicized. She prepared and poured. She waited for people to purchase her product. But her body desperately itched to twitch.

15 "Just one little handstand won't hurt," said Abigail. But her landing sent her crashing into the lemonade stand.

16 She offered to help clean Mrs. Silva's house. She washed windows with willpower. She vacuumed with vigor. She dusted with determination. But she just couldn't resist one little flip while she swept the floor.

17 So Mrs. Silva swept Abigail out the door.

18 "I need a more active job," said Abigail. "Maybe I could be a dog-walker."

19 Her new job worked out fine for a few blocks. But she just couldn't stop herself from doing a quick walkover while she walked the collection of canines.

20 "Abigail, enough!" cried the neighbors when they saw their dogs straying up and down the street.

21 Abigail sighed. It seemed that doing gymnastics always undid her jobs.

22 She wandered toward the gym.

23 "Well," she said, "if I can't do gymnastics at the gym, at least I can watch the others."

24 She seated herself with the spectators. A group of girls no older than Abigail tumbled on the floor mats. Another swung unceasingly on the uneven bars. And a bunch of beginners balanced on the beam.

25 Abigail could barely bear the ache to bounce and bend right along with them.

26 She got up to go. Then she saw the sign:

27 "Wanted: Gymnastics student to be Tots-Class Teacher Assistant. Apply at the front desk."

28 Abigail made it to the desk in two leaps. "I'd like to apply for the Tots-Class Teacher Assistant," she said. "I see," said the woman at the desk. "Are you a student here?"

29 "Not yet," said Abigail.

30 "Can you do gymnastics?" asked the woman.

31 Abigail did a roundoff right then and there.

32 "It appears you are qualified," said the woman. "I think you may be just what we're looking for."

33 Abigail smiled.

34 “There is one thing,” said the woman.

35 “What is it?” asked Abigail.

36 “I’m afraid we don’t pay in money. We pay with free classes. Would you still be interested?”

37 Abigail straddle-jumped so high that there was no doubt about her answer. In fact, she was so happy that she did handsprings all the way home.

38 Abigail spent every afternoon at the gym, teaching and tumbling, assisting and arching, tutoring and twisting. So by the time she got home each day, she’d had her fill of gymnastics.

39 Her father was happy. Her mother was happy. Her brother, Sam, was happy. And Abigail was happiest of all.

40 After that, the only place Abigail heard anyone say “Abigail, enough!” was at the gym—at closing time.

Directions: Answer the following questions. If you need more space to write an answer, write your answer on your own paper.

191 How does Abigail first visiting the gym affect the events of the story?

A She realizes that the classes cost too much.

B She learns different types of moves.

C She learns that there is a job she wants.

D She realizes there are other girls like her.

192 Which sentence describes what is shown in the illustration at the end of the story?

A "Abigail straddle-jumped so high that there was no doubt about her answer."

B "In fact, she was so happy that she did handsprings all the way home."

C "Abigail spent every afternoon at the gym, teaching and tumbling, assisting and arching, tutoring and twisting."

D "So by the time she got home each day, she'd had her fill of gymnastics."

193 At the beginning of the story, the members of her family repeat the phrase "Abigail, enough!" What is the effect of this repetition? How does it show Abigail's problem? Use details from the story to support your answer.

194 Read the sentences from paragraph 6.

> ***"Abigail's body begged to bounce. Her legs longed to leap. Her muscles were meant to move. So Abigail had no choice but to look for somewhere new to bend and bounce, twist and twirl, leap and lunge."***

How does the author's language emphasize how Abigail needs to keep moving? Give **three** examples of phrases used in the paragraph in your answer.

195 Abigail tries three different ways to make money. Complete the chart below by adding the reason that each way does not work out.

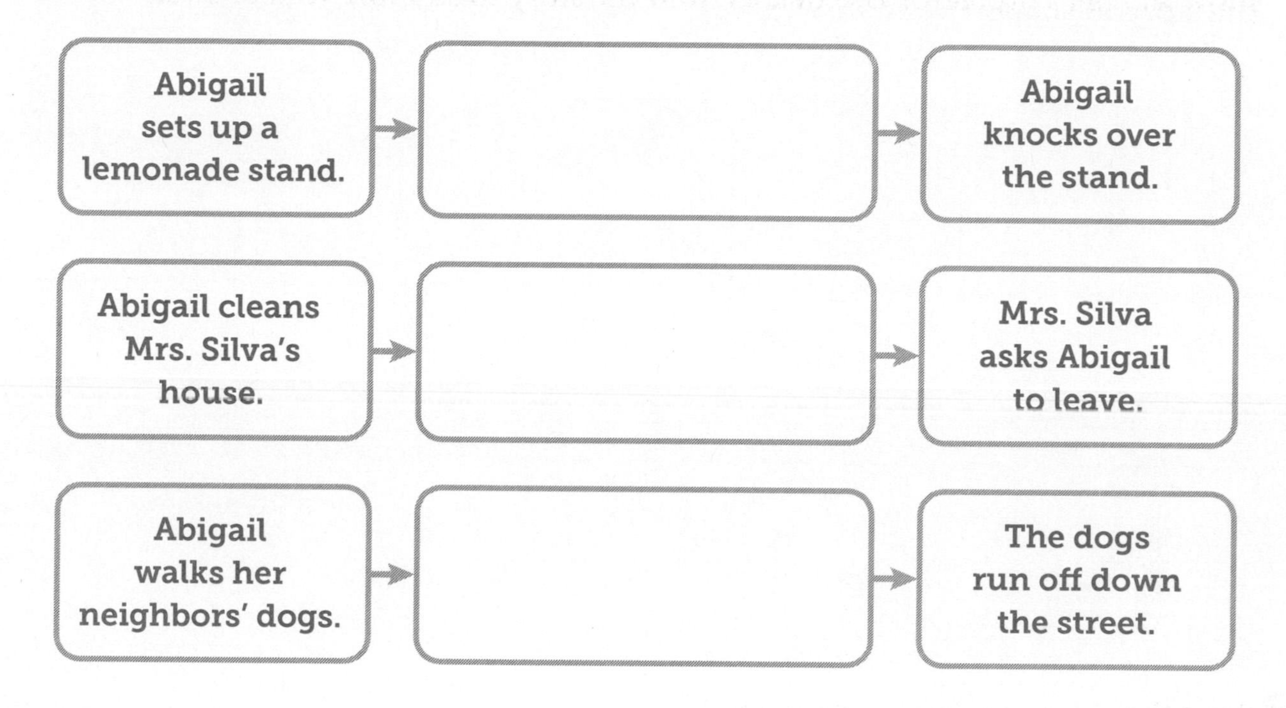

196 In paragraph 27, the author describes how Abigail saw a sign for a teacher assistant job. How do Abigail's words and actions show that she is keen to get the job? Use at least **two** details from the story to support your answer.

197 How is the teaching job different from the other ways Abigail tried to make money? How does this help explain why the job works out? Use details from the story to support your answer.

198 Look closely at the illustration at the beginning of the story. Explain how it shows what Abigail is like and how she affects her family members. Use details from the story to support your answer.

199 The main problem for Abigail and her family is solved when she gets the teaching assistant job. Explain why this job is a perfect solution for Abigail and for her family. Use details from the story to support your answer.

Planning Space

You can complete the chart below to help plan your answer.

	Main Problem	How the Problem is Solved
Abigail		
Abigail's Family		

200 Abigail can be described as a determined person who does not let anything stop her. Explain how you can tell that Abigail is determined. Give **three** examples of actions that show that she is determined in your answer.

Planning Space

You can complete the graphic organizer below to help plan your answer.

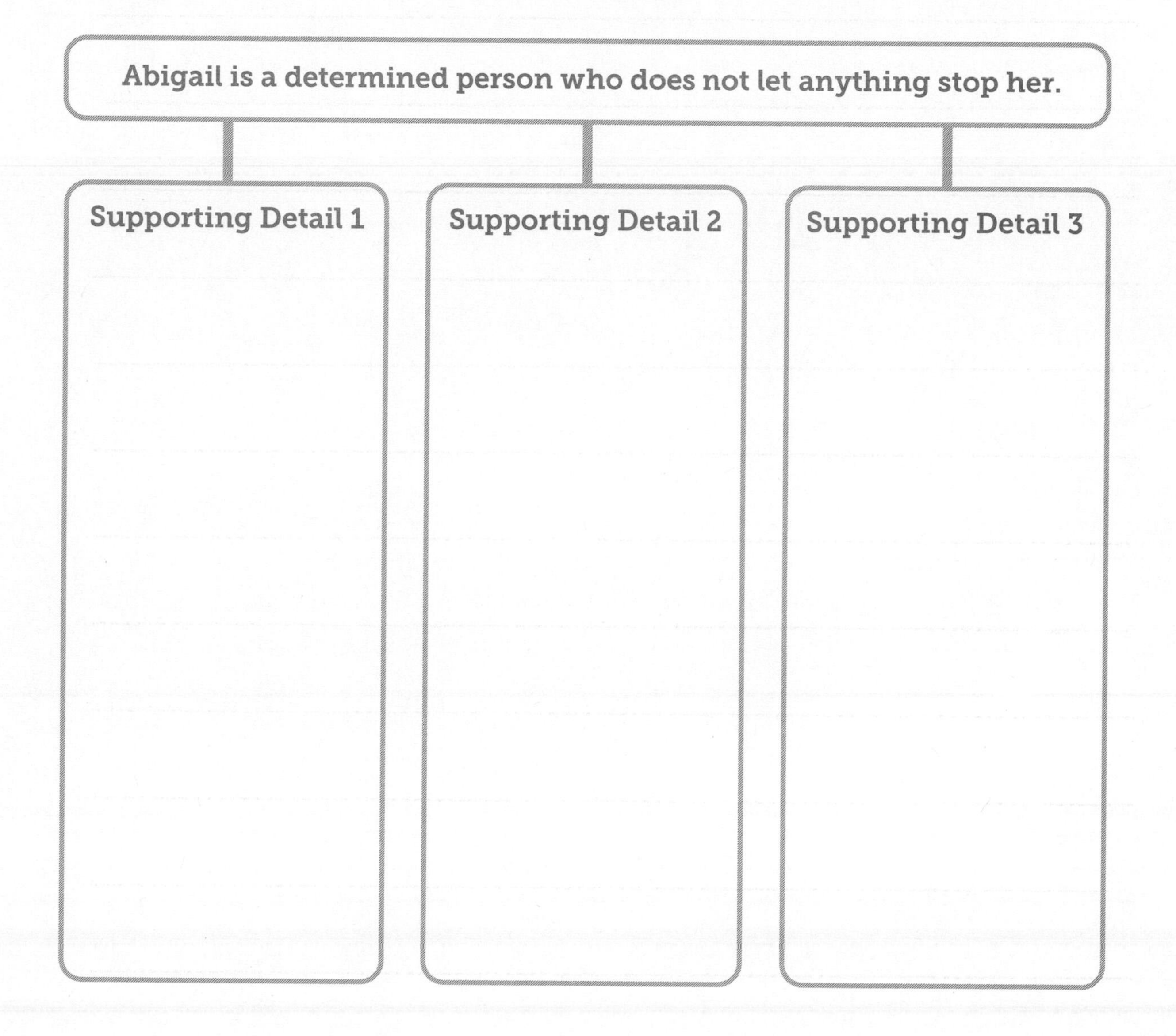

Directions: Read the passage. Then answer the questions that follow it.

Gerbils Morphing

By Dani Sneed

1 An odd squeak startled my son, Kyle, as he passed the gerbil cage. He lifted the screen lid and peered in at Rosey and Stinky.

2 To his surprise the squeaking came from beneath Rosey. She had a bunch of wiggling pink legs sticking out from under her.

3 "Mom, come quick!" yelled Kyle. "Rosey had babies!" Kyle pointed as I entered his room. "Look. They're teeny. They don't have fur."

4 I joined Kyle staring through the glass at the tiny creatures.

5 Several months before, we had gone to the pet store to buy one gerbil. The store owner explained that wild Mongolian gerbils are community animals. Gerbils are happier living together. Two boys would be happy together, and so would two girls. We had picked a boy and a girl, hoping to raise baby gerbils. As the weeks rolled into months, we had given up on the idea of babies.

Surprise!

6 As Rosey left the nest, we gasped at the first sight of the baby gerbils. They lay in the soft bedding. I counted five pups.

7 One newborn was lying on his back. With his pink skin, he looked like a piglet. His eyes were not open yet, and two big black eyes showed through his eyelids. Two bumps showed where his ears

would soon grow. A curious white oval on the side of his tummy was a stomach full of milk. A tiny scab was a future belly button. We wanted to pick up the babies, but we didn't. That might have alarmed the new mother.

8 After a few minutes, the baby surprised us by curling and straightening his body until he rolled to his feet. On unsteady legs he crawled until he bumped into a warm body. Then he cuddled up next to his brothers and sisters.

9 "Let's keep a log of the changes the babies go through," I said.

10 Kyle found a notebook on his desk. "They will have to morph a lot to look like Rosey and Stinky."

11 The next day Kyle brought me to the cage saying, "They are changing colors!"

12 Four of the babies had dark shadows on their backs. One was still pink. We guessed the shadow was fur growing underneath the skin. But why was one pink?

On the Move

13 Before they were a week old, their ears began to stick out. The pups also started wandering around the cage, sniffing, and feeling with their whiskers. Rosey put them back in the nest, where she and Stinky licked them clean. Straying from the nest can be dangerous for mammal babies because they need their mother's milk and warmth.

Baby Gerbils' Growth Log

Day 1– Five babies, all pink, no fur. Eyes are shut. They sleep most of the time.

Day 2– Back shows beginning of fur. Four pups are black. One is still pink.

Day 6– Ears are no longer flat on the head.

Day 8– Thin fur on back. Whiskers are noticeable.

Day 10– One baby died.

Day 13– Fur now on underside. Pups walk around the cage and still sleep a lot. Some fur on tails.

Day 17– Eyes opening.

Day 22– Pups eat food from bowl.

Day 35– Pups go to their new homes.

14 Kyle enjoyed the responsibility of caring for the new family. He couldn't wait for the pups to be old enough for him to play with them.

15 When they were eight days old, their sleek soft fur came in. Four had black fur, and the pink one now had white fur.

16 Every night Kyle gave the parents fresh gerbil food and celery. He picked up Stinky to stroke his back. He made sure all the babies were in the nest. Even so, on day ten Kyle found the smallest and thinnest baby lying still in the nest. He couldn't help feeling sad and guilty that it had died, even though he had given all of them the best care.

Ready to Go

17 At three weeks old, the pups scurried with new speed. They had their eyes open.

18 Rosey had given up trying to put the pups back in the nest. Finally, they were old enough to come out to play. Kyle gently put all four in the dry bathtub with some boxes to explore. We laughed as they scampered around, dug holes through the cardboard, and tunneled through paper-towel rolls.

19 At thirty-five days old, the baby gerbils had made amazing changes. They now ran in the exercise wheel, ate seeds from the food bowl, and had even started gnawing on paper-towel rolls. These darling miniature gerbils were independent, playful, and ready for a new home.

20 Wow, what changes they had made in just a little more than a month! Gerbils morphing!

When the gerbil pups were one day old, they had no hair. They slept almost all the time.

Here, they were four days old. We could see the beginnings of their fur, and their "bumps" were growing into ears.

At the age of fourteen days, they all had fur and whiskers. The ears were more fully developed.

This twenty-day-old pup could see. We had to hold it carefully because it could also jump and hurt itself.

Directions: Answer the following questions. If you need more space to write an answer, write your answer on your own paper.

201 What does the word *morphing* mean?

A playing

B sleeping

C changing

D caring

202 In which sentence does the author state a fact about Kyle?

A "Kyle enjoyed the responsibility of caring for the new family."

B "He couldn't wait for the pups to be old enough for him to play with them."

C "Every night Kyle gave the parents fresh gerbil food and celery."

D "He couldn't help feeling sad and guilty that it had died, even though he had given all of them the best care."

203 The article describes the gerbils from when they were born on Day 1 to Day 35. Complete the chart below by describing each feature. You can use information in the article, the photographs, or the log to complete the chart.

Feature	On Day 1	By Day 35
Ears		
Fur		
Whiskers		
Eyes		

204 In paragraph 5, the author tells how the gerbils are "community animals." What does this term mean? How does the information in the paragraph help show the meaning of this? Use details from the article to support your answer.

205 Read these sentences from the article.

> ***"Four of the babies had dark shadows on their backs. One was still pink. We guessed the shadow was fur growing underneath the skin. But why was one pink?"***

What was found to be different about the babies later? How did this answer the question of why one was pink? Use details from the article to support your answer.

206 As well as looking different, the way the gerbils behaved changed as they got older. Explain how the behavior was different on Day 35 compared to Day 1. Use details from the article to support your answer.

207 How is the information organized in the growth log and in the photographs on page 232? Is this organization suited to the purpose of the growth log and the photographs? Use details from the article to support your answer.

208 In the section "On the Move," the author explains that Kyle felt guilty when one of the gerbils died. Does the author feel that Kyle should feel guilty? Use details from the section to support your conclusion.

209 The log gives facts about what Kyle observed. How would the log have been different if Kyle had also included his thoughts in the log? Explain which **two** entries you think would be most different and explain why. Use details from the article and the log to support your answer.

Planning Space

You can write notes, make a list, or draw a chart to help plan your answer.

210 The article suggests that Kyle and his mother enjoyed the experience described. What do you think they enjoyed most about the experience? Use at least **three** details from the article to support your answer.

Planning Space

You can write notes, make a list, or draw a chart to help plan your answer.

Directions: Read the passage. Then answer the questions that follow it.

Two Friends, Three Friends

By Eileen Spinelli

1 2 on a seesaw,
Jack and me.
2 on a seesaw,
can't be 3.

2 Jack's my best friend.
I'm his, too.
2 in the sandbox.
2 at the zoo.

3 Jack throws the ball,
I toss it back.
Back and forth—
just me and Jack.

4 Carrie sees us,
wants to play.
"3's too many
friends," I say.

5 Jack and I
climb in a crate.
Carrie watches
from the gate.

6 The crate's a train
for 2 to ride.
3 just wouldn't
fit inside.

7 Jack and I
find two big rocks.
We put them in
a cardboard box.

8 Jack lifts his end.
I lift mine.
Starting out
we 2 do fine.

9 Then we drop it.
Then we stumble.
This box of rocks
is heavy! Grumble!

10 That's when Carrie
comes along.
"I can help.
I'm big and strong!"

11 3 make hard work
fast and fun.
Milk and cookies
when we're done.

12 3 friends now:
me, Jack, and Carrie
baking mud pies ...
"Hi!" says Barry.

Directions: Answer the following questions. If you need more space to write an answer, write your answer on your own paper.

211 Which stanza states the relationship between Jack and the speaker?

A Stanza 1

B Stanza 2

C Stanza 3

D Stanza 4

212 Read these lines from the first stanza.

> ***"2 on a seesaw,***
> ***can't be 3."***

These lines tell the opinion of

A Carrie

B Jack

C the author

D the speaker

213 The poem describes Jack and the speaker doing different activities together. Which **two** activities described are best for just two people? Explain why you chose those activities. Use details from the poem to support your answer.

214 How does Carrie most likely feel in stanza 4? How did Jack's actions make her feel that way? Use details from the poem to support your answer.

215 The illustration of Jack and the speaker playing in the box shows Carrie watching from behind the gate. How does showing Carrie behind the gate help show the relationship between Carrie and the boys? Use details from the poem to support your answer.

216 In stanza 9, what does the word *grumble* mean? What does the word show about the boys? Use details from the poem to support your answer.

217 In which scene does Carrie try to make friends with the boys again? Explain why this is a good choice. Use details from the poem to support your answer.

218 Describe the rhythm of stanza 11. What does the rhythm suggest about how Jack and the speaker feel about having a third friend? Use details from the poem to support your answer.

219 Think about the events of the poem and how they are described. Who do you think the poet wrote the poem for? What do you think the poet wants those readers to learn? Use details from the poem to support your answer.

Planning Space

You can write notes, make a list, or draw a chart to help plan your answer.

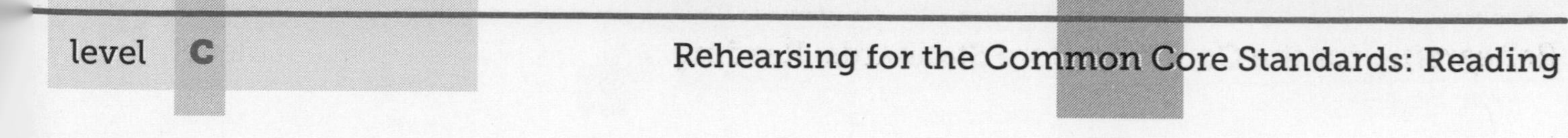

220 The poem ends with a boy named Barry saying hi. What do you think will happen next? Explain whether or not you think the three friends will ask Barry to play with them. Use details from the poem to support your answer.

Planning Space

You can write notes, make a list, or draw a chart to help plan your answer.

Directions: Read the following two passages. Then answer the questions that follow.

Face to Face with Barn Owls

By Chris Dietel

1 One day I was hiking in the mountains when I made a great discovery. Actually, my dog did. She stopped in her path. Her nose pointed to a small cave on a steep slope.

Baby Barn Owls

2 I peered into the cave. Deep inside sat four small owl chicks. Each one was about the size of my fist. They had no feathers yet, just fine white hair called *down*. They raised their heads slowly and clumsily. They looked at me with squinting eyes.

3 I took a few pictures. Then I climbed away and waited for the parents to return. Soon a large bird swooped into the nest. It had a ring of feathers around its face that made the shape of a heart. I knew it was a barn owl.

4 The barn owl makes its nest in caves and in hollows of trees. Sometimes it chooses old buildings or barns. That's how it got its most common name, barn owl. Some people think its face looks like a monkey's face. That's why people sometimes call it the monkey-faced owl.

Growing Up

5 Weeks later, I visited the four chicks again. They greeted me with a very loud *HISSSSS*. The sound hurt my ears! Now the chicks were big and fluffy. Feathers were just starting to grow around their faces. After a few minutes, the chicks relaxed. I took some pictures. The chicks stared at me with dark glassy eyes. They moved their heads slowly from side to side. I then left the area so the adults could return.

6 Adult barn owls hunt for food at night. They can see much better in the dark than humans can. Barn owls also have amazing hearing. They use their sensitive ears to catch their prey. They can catch a small rodent, like a mouse, without even seeing it. The owl snatches the mouse with the sharp claws on its feet.

7 On my last visit to the nest, the chicks had become adults. They burst out of the cave and flew away before I got too close. I had been very lucky to get face to face with those owls—when they were big fluffy chicks. Now they were adult barn owls, flying free.

An Eye Out for Owls

By Scott Linstead

1 It was a September morning, and I was lugging a large camera through tall pines. The area was perfect for a family of great horned owls. The trees were well spaced for the owls' large wingspans. But it was the third time I'd come to this spot, and I had not yet seen any owls.

2 Suddenly, I heard noisy crows in the distance. Crows often get together in a tree and make loud noises for no obvious reason. But sometimes they squawk a lot when they come across a raptor, a bird that hunts animals. Owls are raptors. I followed the noise and found a great horned owl.

3 People are often surprised to learn that many owls live in ordinary neighborhoods. One February day, I said to my friend as we drove along, "Stop the car. There's a screech owl in that tree!"

4 The tree was on a front lawn. Even though the driver doubted me, he stopped the car. Sure enough, an eastern screech owl stared back at us from a hole in the tree. Over the years, I have become used to looking carefully at trees for screech owls.

5 For many years, I had wanted to photograph a long-eared owl. I had often seen these birds in the wild, but they are hard to photograph. They hide in thick trees during the day. Like other small owls, they can be eaten by larger owls and other raptors.

6 One winter day, I was at a spot where three long-eared owls liked to roost in cedar trees. It was the first time I had a good view of these owls! Each one was no taller than a paper-towel tube.

7 I set up my camera as quickly as I could. One long-eared owl stared back at me just long enough that I could take a few pictures. Then it hopped onto a more hidden branch.

8 The barred owl is a fairly large bird with deep black eyes. It allows you to get closer than other owls do. But if you happen to be a great horned owl, it won't stick around very long. It's been reported that the great horned owl might eat the barred owl!

9 One November, I came face to face with a barred owl in a swampy, wooded area. Luckily, there were no great horned owls around. This spot had been the winter home of a barred owl for many years. The only years it was not seen were those when a great horned owl lived in the area.

10 The fall and winter are great times to look for owls. When leaves are gone from the trees, the owls' perches are much easier to spot. Keep your eyes open for owls this season.

Directions: Use "Face to Face with Barn Owls" to answer the following questions. If you need more space to write an answer, write your answer on your own paper.

221 How does the author know that the baby owls are barn owls?

A by where he finds them

B by the shape of the mother's face

C by how small the chicks are

D by what color they are

222 All of the following are ways the owl chicks are different on the second visit EXCEPT

A they are larger

B they can move their heads well

C they have feathers

D they are able to fly

223 What is the main reason the author was lucky to see the barn owls when they were chicks?

A Barn owls are usually only seen at night.

B There are few barn owls left in the world.

C Adult barn owls do not let people near them.

D Barn owls do not often have babies.

224 The author describes his experience, but also includes facts about barn owls. Do you feel these facts made the article more interesting? Use at least **two** examples of facts given to support your answer.

Directions: Use "An Eye Out for Owls" to answer the following questions. If you need more space to write an answer, write your answer on your own paper.

225 In paragraphs 3 and 4, the author tells a story about seeing a screech owl. Why does the author tell this story? What main idea does it support? Use details from the article to support your answer.

226 The article describes many owls the author has seen. Complete the web below by naming **three** more owls and listing where each one was seen.

Owls Spotted

Name	Location
great horned owl	in tall pines

227 How can you tell that the author is very keen to photograph owls? Use at least **three** details from the article to support your answer.

Directions: Use both "Face to Face with Barn Owls" and "An Eye Out for Owls" to answer the following questions. If you need more space to write an answer, write your answer on your own paper.

228 Read these sentences from "An Eye Out for Owls."

> ***"But sometimes they squawk a lot when they come across a raptor, a bird that hunts animals. Owls are raptors."***

How does the information in "Face to Face with Barn Owls" support the idea that owls are raptors? Use details from both articles to support your answer.

229 In the first two paragraphs of "An Eye Out for Owls," the author describes spotting a great horned owl. How is the way the author found the owl similar to how the author of "Face to Face with Barn Owls" found the chicks? Use details from both articles to support your answer.

230 In both articles, the author describes his experiences spotting and taking photographs of owls. How are their experiences similar? How is the way they feel about owls similar? Use information from the article to support your answer.

Planning Space

You can complete the chart below to help plan your answer.

	Author of "Face to Face with Barn Owls"	Author of "An Eye Out for Owls"
What owls did he spot?		
How did he spot the owls?		
How does he feel about the owls?		

Directions: Read the following two passages. Then answer the questions that follow.

The Cave That Talked
A Tale from the *Panchatantra*

Retold by Jyoti Singh Visvanath

The Panchatantra *is a collection of stories written long ago in India. A teacher wrote them to show his students, three young princes, how to live wisely.*

1 Long ago, deep in a forest, a jackal discovered a cave. He decided to make it his home. He left his cave every morning to hunt for food, and returned in the evening.

2 In the same forest lived an old lion. He had once been the king of the forest, but a younger, stronger lion had taken his place. The old lion wandered through the forest looking for food. But as he was too old to hunt, he often had to go hungry.

3 One day the lion wandered off his usual path in the forest. He tripped on a branch and tumbled down a small hill, landing near the mouth of a cave. The lion picked himself up slowly and walked to the cave's entrance. He looked inside. There seemed to be no one there. He sniffed. Aha! His nose told him that an animal lived in this cave. Sooner or later it would return home.

4 The lion licked his lips. "At last I'll get something to eat," he thought. "I will hide in this cave and eat the animal that lives here as soon as it enters."

5 Late in the afternoon the jackal returned to his cave. As he walked toward the entrance, he noticed something strange. Near the mouth of the cave were footprints of some big animal. He saw that the footprints went into his cave but did not come out. That meant the animal was still inside. He wondered what to do. Then he had an idea.

6 "Oh, cave, my dear cave," he shouted. "Please talk to me." There was no reply. "Why are you so quiet?" called the jackal. "You promised to greet me every day when I came home." Still no reply. "All right! If you will not speak to me, I will go to the other cave that talks," said the jackal. He made sounds to show that he was leaving.

7 The lion sat in the cave, wondering what was happening. He heard the jackal call out to the cave, but the cave did not reply. "The cave must be keeping quiet because I am here," thought the lion. "If I call out a greeting, the jackal will come into the cave, and I can eat him up."

8 The lion roared out a greeting. The sound bounced off the walls and came out through the mouth of the cave. It was loud enough to be heard by all the animals in the forest.

9 The jackal quickly understood that a lion was hiding in his cave. Chuckling to himself, he said, "Long years through these woods I've walked, but I've never heard a cave that talked." Then he ran far from the cave to find himself a new home.

The Unwelcome Neighbor
A Tale from the *Panchatantra*

Retold by Santhini Govindan

The Panchatantra *is a collection of stories written long ago in India. Like* Aesop's Fables, *the stories teach how to live a wise life.*

1 Once upon a time a pair of crows came across a huge old banyan tree. The tree had strong branches and a wonderful roof of green leaves that provided shade from the sun. It seemed like the perfect place to build a nest.

2 The crows immediately set to work. Soon a round nest was hidden high among the leaves of the tree, ready for the eggs that Mother Crow would lay.

3 One day, a huge black snake slithered past the banyan. He noticed a deep, dark hole at the bottom of the tree, and he decided to make it his home.

4 This alarmed the crows. Father Crow discussed the matter with the other animals who lived in the banyan tree. "Beware of the snake," they said. "He is dangerous. He will wait for a chance to eat up all your babies!"

5 When Mother Crow heard this, she began to cry. "How can I lay my eggs, knowing that the snake will gobble up all my babies as soon as they are hatched?" she asked Father Crow. "I want to leave! Let's go far away and make a new nest."

6 "No, we must not leave," said Father Crow. "The banyan tree is the best place for us to live. I will find some way to drive away the snake."

7 Mother Crow was reassured by Father Crow's words. She laid seven eggs, and before long there were seven baby crows in the nest. They quickly grew big and fat under Mother Crow's watchful eye. Their noisy chirping could be heard all over the

banyan tree. The snake heard it, too, and slithered up and down the branches of the tree every day, searching for the crows' nest.

8 "Please do something to drive away the snake," Mother Crow begged. "Otherwise he will soon discover our precious babies and eat them up!"

9 Father Crow decided to ask a wise old fox for help. The fox listened to the crow's tale of woe and then came up with a brilliant plan. He told the two crows to go to the river the next morning. The ladies of the royal household would be bathing there. Their clothes and jewels would be lying on the riverbank, watched over by servants.

10 "Pick up a necklace and fly home," said the fox. "Be sure to make a loud noise so that the servants will follow you. When you reach the tree, drop the necklace into the snake's hole."

11 The crows did exactly as the fox had told them. Mother Crow snatched a ruby necklace in her beak and flew away. Father Crow cawed loudly to attract the servants' attention.

12 The servants chased Mother Crow, and as they reached the banyan tree, they saw her drop the necklace into the snake's hole.

13 When the servants tried to take the necklace out of the hole with a stick, the angry snake came out hissing. The servants drew back in alarm, and then tried to beat the snake. But the snake, afraid for his life, slithered away as fast as he could and never came back to the banyan tree. Mother and Father Crow lived there happily for many years and raised many babies, too.

Directions: Use "The Cave That Talked" to answer the following questions. If you need more space to write an answer, write your answer on your own paper.

231 The introduction at the start of the story shows that the story is a

A myth

B fairy tale

C fable

D legend

232 Based on your answer to question 231, what main feature described shows the genre?

A There are many stories in the collection.

B There are royal characters in the stories.

C The stories were written to teach lessons.

D The stories were written long ago in India.

233 How does the jackal first learn that there is an animal in his cave?

A by smelling the animal

B by seeing the footprints

C by asking the cave

D by hearing the roar

234 In paragraph 9, the jackal says that he has never heard a cave that talked. Why does the jackal say that his cave does talk earlier in the story? Use details from the story to support your answer.

Directions: Use "The Unwelcome Neighbor" to answer the following questions. If you need more space to write an answer, write your answer on your own paper.

235 Is Mother Crow afraid of the snake because of her own safety? What does this show about what Mother Crow is like? Use details from the story to support your answer.

236 Read these sentences from paragraph 4.

> ***"Beware of the snake," they said. "He is dangerous. He will wait for a chance to eat up all your babies!"***

How do the events of the story show that the animals are right to give this warning? Use details from the story to support your answer.

237 The illustration is included to represent a scene in the story. Complete the chart below by giving **three** examples of details from the story shown in the illustration.

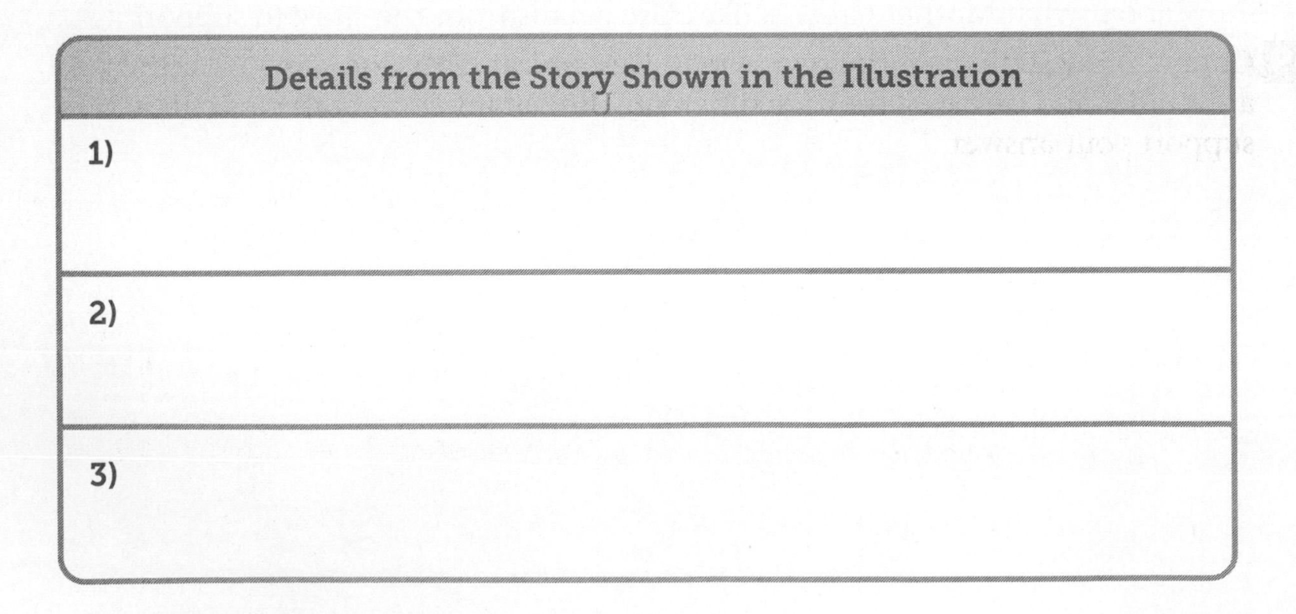

Details from the Story Shown in the Illustration
1)
2)
3)

Directions: Use both "The Cave That Talked" and "The Unwelcome Neighbor" to answer the following questions. If you need more space to write an answer, write your answer on your own paper.

238 The introduction to "The Unwelcome Neighbor" states that the stories are like *Aesop's Fables*. Describe **two** ways both stories are like fables. Use details from both stories to support your answer.

239 Compare the settings of the two stories. Describe at least **one** way the settings are similar and **one** way they are different. Use details from both stories to support your answer.

240 Both stories describe characters who have a problem and come up with a clever way to solve the problem. Describe the problem in each story and the plan that is used to solve it. Which plan do you feel is the most clever? Explain why you made that choice. Use information from both stories to support your answer.

Planning Space

You can complete the chart below to help plan your answer.

	The Cave That Talked	The Unwelcome Neighbor
What is the main problem?		
What is the plan used to solve the main problem?		
What makes the plan clever?		